# Crystal Set Projects:
## 15 Radio Projects You Can Build

# Crystal Set Projects:
## 15 Radio Projects You Can Build

**The Xtal Set Society**
www.midnightscience.com
1-800-927-1771

Printed in the United States of America
ISBN: 1-887736-06-9

A special thanks to the members of the Xtal Set Society for their enthusiasm and dedication.

# Table of Contents

Preface                                                           11

Introduction                                                      13

Low Budget Xtal Set
    William Simes                             21

A Loop Antenna Crystal Set
    Michael Mauser                            29

Benjamin and David Goldenberg's Very-Fine
Old-Time Crystal Radio
    Benjamin and David Goldenberg             41

The Directional Loop DX Xtal Set
    Joseph Cooper                             53

The Den Two Crystal Radio
    Alan Klase                                65

How to Build and Use a High Performance Crystal Set
    Lance Borden                              71

A Homemade Variable Capacitor and a Trap Tuned Set
    Eric Hudson                               85

Build a Matchbox Crystal Radio
    Jim Clark                                 95

A Krystal Kludge
    William Simes                             103

A Triple Tuned Crystal Set
    Greg Constant                                     111

My Best Set Yet
    Carl Davis                                         121

Yesterday's Circuit Today's Parts
    William Simes                                 125

A Magic Coil for Crystal Radios
    George Hails                                   131

Antenna-Ground System
    Mark Zechar                                 141

The Design and Construction of a Ferrite Loopstick
Inductor for an AM Broadcast Receiver
    Ross Wollrab                             149

Vendor List                                       155

The Xtal Set Society, Membership and Books     157

# Preface

Crystal Set Radios? Yes, that's right. Over 90 years since their invention, Xtal Sets are still capturing people's attention. The Xtal Set Society was founded in 1991 and is dedicated to building and experimenting with crystal set radios. When I was first asked to run the Society, I wasn't sure how many folks still liked building these little sets, but I soon found out that Xtal sets have a following all over the globe. We've been getting faxes and e-mails from around the world at all times of the day and night saying, "Who the heck are you guys? Can I get more information?" One customer e-mailed us from our web page, "I was so flabbergasted to find a society of Xtal set builders that I fell off my chair." This theme seems to reoccur throughout our mail as Xtal set builders are joyous to find a home while still not quite believing it, "You mean there are others out there like me? A whole society?" I love to answer, "Yes! I'll send you a copy of the newsletter." Our members include engineers, electronics enthusiasts, amateur radio operators, antique radio buffs, science teachers, and many others. Every other month the Society publishes a newsletter with projects and articles sent in by our members.

This book is a collection of crystal radio projects designed by members of the Xtal Set Society. Our members kept writing and requesting, "More projects, more projects!" We decided to challenge the members to build and design sets that people would enjoy recreating, and they took the challenge by sending us more xtal set stuff than even we wanted. We tried to choose projects of various designs and difficulty so that everyone could learn something while building the radios in this book.

We have attempted to place the projects roughly in order of difficulty, putting the simplest sets up front and the most challenging in the back. The first four projects are great for building with kids at home, in the classroom, or at scouting. Some of the projects in the back section are for the truly diehard enthusiast, and they include details such as building cases and adding finishing touches. The last three projects include information about making special coils and a ground system.

The projects are written by different authors, so each writer has his own style and organization. Read through a project completely before beginning and make sure you have all the parts and equipment. Although many of the authors provide a parts lists with suggested vendors, these vendors are not the only option, and a number of the items can be purchased from various stores and dealers. You will find a list of vendors at the back of the book.

A word to the beginner. Building crystal sets requires some patience; experimenting and tinkering often bring results. The most common problem for the beginner is getting a good ground, so if you have a problem getting a set to work check all your connections and your ground first. If you try everything the author suggests and you still can't get a set to work, try finding the nearest amateur radio operator (also called "hams") or amateur radio club. Just about every ham I've ever met says he started out in radio by building a crystal set, and they enjoy sharing their love of radio.

If this book inspires you to start designing your own sets, then by all means send in the plans! There just might be a Volume 2.... Have fun!

Rebecca Hewes
The Xtal Set Society, 1997

# Introduction
by Phil Anderson and Rebecca Hewes

## What Is a Crystal Radio Set?

Crystal set radios pick up AM radio without batteries or electricity. In the simplest terms, the broadcast station puts out enough power in the form of a radio signal to be picked up by a crystal set. The set's antenna captures this electromagnetic energy, and the signal then passes through the crystal detector and comes out as audio in the earphones. This mysterious process first intrigued great inventors such as Braun, Marconi, and Pickard, and it continues to fascinate electronics buffs, amateur radio operators, and engineers today.

The hobby of building and listening to crystal radio had its first and biggest craze in the 1920's. Once radio stations began broadcasting all over the country, people began buying and building crystal radio kits. At that time a true mineral crystal was used as the detector. The most popular crystal was galena, and a fine piece of wire called a "cat's whisker" was used to touch the crystal and find the "hot spot" on the rock where a station would come in. These days, many hobbyists use the modern day diode instead of a crystal, but there are still experimenters who strive for the thrill of getting Radio Japan on a rock.

In the 1950's the hobby enjoyed a revival of sorts; fathers remembered building the sets as kids in the 1920's, and they wanted their sons to build them also. A surprising number of men who grew up in the 1950's built crystal radio sets with their fathers and as Boy Scouts. During the 1950's all sorts of crystal set kits became available, including some on the backs of cereal boxes. Now the hobby is still going strong as those boys from the 50's have become fathers and want to pass on this radio magic. (Lets teach the girls this time, guys!)

## What the Crystal Set Can Teach Us

The crystal set is the basis for modern day radio and communications equipment; the basics it embodies live on in a wide variety of radio systems. For this reason, a study of crystal sets is a great place to start to build a foundation in radio electronics.

If you build a short wave (high frequency) AM set, you'll also experience firsthand the constantly varying state of the ionosphere. The signals from distant stations will ebb and flow, particularly at night.

Many of our members are interested in the crystal set because of its simplicity and complexity; it contains few parts but exhibits many concepts. Crystal sets are a great tool for teaching, and they are a superb hobby. If you haven't built a set before, review the following sections on a basic set and on reading schematics.

### A Basic Crystal Set

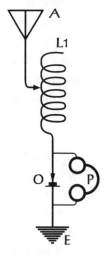

Figure 1:
Simple set

A simple set is shown in schematic form in Figure 1. It consists of just five parts: an antenna, an antenna coil, a detector, a pair of headphones, and ground. It's been built, perhaps, a million times, on farms, in attics, in living rooms, and in fox holes over the years. Builders used this set to listen to early broadcasts such as The Shadow, the Dempsey fight, or Armed Forces News!

The antenna (A) is simply a long piece of wire. For stations broadcasting in the 550-1500 Kilohertz (kHz) band, the AM band on your pocket radio, 75 feet or so works quite well. This long wire antenna, often called an end-fed, is attached to the set at one end and to a tree, pole, or whatever at its other end.

The antenna coil (L1) is added to resonate the antenna and, for more complex sets, to match the antenna to the detector and headphones.

The coil can be wound on a cylindrical form, a match box, a Quaker Oats box, or even take the shape of a spider web. Cotton covered wire was used for sets built in the twenties; we use enameled or plastic coated wire today.

The remaining parts, the detector (O), headphones (P), and ground (E) work together to recover audio from the radio signal. The radio signal is converted to audio by the detector, called a diode today, and audio is heard in the headphones. This process is called rectification and is basic to all radio receivers.

## Reading Schematics

Many of the schematics in this book are produced in the 1920's style. Although they sometimes look daunting, even the novice can figure out the basics of a circuit if they are familiar with the individual symbols. By connecting them together, like drawing a dot-to-dot picture, you can create circuit plans. A plan is simply a wiring schematic, showing the parts and the wires interconnecting them. Figure 1 is an example of a crystal radio schematic.

The drawing symbols are often based on the shape or the action of the part they represent. The antenna is no exception. Antennas built by radio pioneers consisted, often, of sets of parallel wires, tied together at a common point (a). The symbol used today is simplified (b). Coils are made by winding wire on a form, typically cylindrical, so the symbol is a spiral (c). Capacitors are made by stacking metal plates, with air or some other non-conducting material between

(a) antenna     (b) antenna

(c) coil

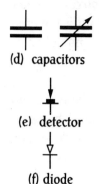

(d) capacitors

the plates; hence, they are drawn as two lines, one above the other (d). An arrow through the plates denotes that the part, once wired into a set, can be adjusted.

(e) detector

(f) diode

The detector symbol (e) is also derived from its physical origin, a sharpened or thin wire pressed lightly against a hunk of galena crystal mounted in a holder. The symbol for the modern day detector (f), the diode, is similar but simplified; its origin is not as clearly displayed. So much for modern brevity!

The headphone symbol (g) includes two circles which represent phones, one for each ear. The loop denotes the band that goes over your head and holds the phones together. The line also indicates that the phones are wired in series. Crystal set headphones have an impedance of 2,000 to 4,000 ohms and are not equivalent to today's 8 ohm sets for stereo systems. The old 2,000 ohm headphones can still be purchased at radio meets, and from antique radio dealers, and they really work great. Another option is to purchase a crystal earplug from an electronics store (see the vendor section at the end of this book).

(g) headphones

(h) resistor

(i) ground

The resistor and ground symbols are the last of the basic symbols. Resistors were originally constructed with wire, and were often wound on a cylindrical form. The zigzag shape of the resistor symbol (h) denotes added wire, resulting in additional resistance (to current flow). The ground symbol (i) is a series of stacked lines, since a good ground can consist of a number of buried, interconnected wires or plates.

Using these symbols, we can draw a representation of any of the crystal sets. The result is a schematic which shows the parts used and how they are wired together.

## Some Notes about Antennas and Ground

Although a long piece of wire strung around the room will often work just fine to pick up a close local station, you'll have more luck picking up stations far away with a more elaborate antenna. 75 feet or more strung outside into a tree works great. **Remember to avoid power lines!** If you want a more permanent set-up, take 75 feet of wire, attach one end as high up as possible in a tree and then attach the other end to the roof or another tree, hang another "lead-in" wire from the middle down to your crystal set.

Ground your set to a cold water pipe by attaching a wire to the pipe and then your set. Another option is to attach a wire to a copper pipe or rod driven into the earth.

## Electronic Theory behind the Crystal Set

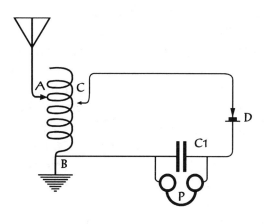

Figure 2: Conductively coupled receiver. A-antenna; B-ground; C-coil; C1-capacitor; D-diode, P-headphones.

You don't have to understand the next few pages of theory to enjoy building and listening to crystal radio, but we have included it for the many teachers and parents who would like to use the crystal set to teach basic radio electronics. Figure 2 is a schematic of the basic conductively coupled crystal set. Let's examine how this basic set works.

The conductively coupled set has been very popular through the years. Its popularity is derived from the fact that it is easy to build, easy to tune, and develops more volume than the basic set of Figure 1, even under less than ideal conditions. This set differs from the basic set in that the detector is wired to the top of the antenna coil or near it instead of at its bottom. It's called the conductively coupled receiver because the detector is wired directly to the antenna coil, unlike many sets that use a transformer coupling magnetically.

The job of the antenna is to convert incoming radio waves into radio frequency current. The electromagnetic waves surround the antenna and induce a current in it. The process is called electromagnetic induction. Of course, all radio waves in the vicinity of the antenna produce currents.

The job of the antenna coil is to help restrict unwanted signals and to boost desired ones. For example, we might wish to listen to a station at 1000 Kilohertz, but we may hear one at 1300 Kilohertz also. The coil works in conjunction with the antenna. The capacitance of the antenna (C) is combined with the inductance of the coil (L) to form a filter. This series tuned "L-C circuit"—often called a tank circuit— reduces signals it is not tuned to and retains the signals to which it is tuned. In effect, the crystal set is tuned by selecting the right coil to match the antenna. These basic sets do a pretty good job; however, they have a limited capability to eliminate the reception of strong stations that are on a frequency near the one we wish to isolate and listen to.

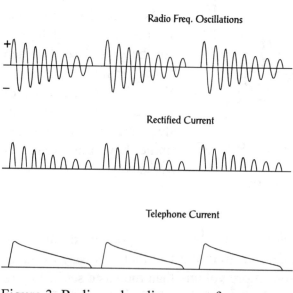

Radio Freq. Oscillations

Rectified Current

Telephone Current

Figure 3: Radio and audio current frequency

The radio frequency (RF) current, produced by the antenna and the coil, is shown graphically in Figure 3, "Radio Frequency

Oscillations". This current will swing alternately positive and negative every radio frequency cycle. For example, if you are listening to an AM station at 1,000 Kilohertz (one megahertz), the current in the antenna will reverse direction one million times each second.

The job of the detector is to eliminate either the positive-going or negative-going portion of this current, and this process is called rectification. For our set in Figure 2, the detector will conduct current when the radio frequency current is positive, but not when it is negative. This is the nature of the detector. Only the positive portion of the RF current, labeled "rectified current" in Figure 3, flows through the diode to the capacitor and headphones. The job of the headphones is to convert this rectified RF current into an audible tones. In the 1920's, the term "telephone current" was often used, rather than "audio current" as "headphones" evolved from telephone earphones.

How do the detector and headphones, working together, accomplish this? Each time the radio signal goes positive, current will flow in the detector. But since the current is pulsating at a radio frequency, the diaphragm in the headphones will not follow it; the fluctuations are simply too fast. Hence, all of the current simply charges the capacitor placed in parallel with the headphones. During the negative portion of the RF cycle, when the diode is off (back biased), the charge on the capacitor leaks off slowly through the headphones. This is denoted by the slow decay (slope) in the telephone current, as shown at the bottom in Figure 3. The diaphragm in the headphones can follow this audio signal so it's audible in the headphones.

The strength of the voltage developed on the capacitor across the headphones follows the amplitude (or peak value) of the RF antenna current. The current developed in the headphones, in turn, is proportional to the capacitor's voltage. Hence, what you hear is the changing amplitude of the RF signal. Radio signals that convey information by varying their amplitude are called amplitude modulated waves (AM)!

That's really the essence of the crystal radio set. It's job is to transform efficiently the radio frequency energy delivered to its antenna to audio energy at the set headphones. The set acts as a converter of radio signals into audio signals; that is, the radio captures the radio signal, filters out unwanted signals, and acts as a rectifier.

# Low Budget Xtal Set
by William Simes

The set described here, built from tinkertoys and a few parts, is intended as a possible class project for a small group of elementary school students. The finished set should be functional for receiving AM stations of 5KW or more from a distance of 6 miles or less. If the classroom structure has a steel frame, the room may be sufficiently shielded to prevent good reception, in which case you should consider operating the set outside on a dry day when the wind is calm.

I invited my second grade neighbor over to try out making this set. She did well but still needed some help winding the wire and stripping insulation. She was so happy with her creation, she phoned her mother to come over to see it and hear it.

Photo 1: Bill's neighbor testing out the set she helped build

Table 1: Materials needed

| From a Tinker toy set[1] | | |
|---|---|---|
| 14 | 10¾ inch dowels | |
| 12 | 2 ⅛ inch dowels | |
| 8 | 7½ inch dowels | |
| 4 | 5 inch dowels | |
| 16 | connector spools | |
| Qty | Description | Suggested Supplier |
| 2 | plastic sheet protector | poly-vu #PV119G |
| 1 | Round-head paper fastener, 1-inch | |
| 1 | 1N34A diode | Radio Shack #276-1123 |
| 5 | Test leads | #278-1156 |
| 50ft. | #20 AWG solid hook-up wire | #278-1216 |
| 1 | Crystal Earphone[2] | Xtal Set Society |
| | Reynolds aluminum foil, 12-inch wide | |
| | Scotch tape | |
| | card table with non-conducting top | |
| | scissors | |

[1]Tinker toys have been around for several generations. Originally, they were all wood with the natural color of the wood. In the 70's the dowels were color coded by length: violet = 10¾, yellow = 2 ⅛, green = 7½, red = 5. Today the parts are made of plastic and are still color coded.

[2]Ideally, the receiver would be high-impedance (2000-ohm) headphones. These are no longer common among currently used headphones, but can be found at radio swap meets and from antique radio dealers. For the classroom an inexpensive alternative is to purchase crystal earplugs. Also new 2000 ohm headsets are available from the XSS and AES, see the vendors section in the back.

## Making the Loop

1. Using the tinker toys, assemble a coil form for the loop antenna as shown in Figure 1. Press the joints together firmly to assure a rigid structure. It is suggested the center square made of the longest dowels be made first, then build from this.

2. On the spool of hook-up wire, use one scissors blade to strip an inch or so of insulation from the exposed wire end.

3. About one foot from the wire end, wrap and tie the hook-up wire to the round tinkertoy at the base of the structure on the right hand side.

4. Wrap 6 turns of wire clockwise on the coil form. Wind the first turn with the wire always close to the connector spools. Make the next turn also close to the connector spools, but on the spool side opposite the first turn. Continue on alternate sides with each successive turn. At the end of turn 6, secure the wire to the round tinkertoy at the base on the left hand side. About a foot from the left base cut the free end of the wire with the scissors. With a blade of the scissors, strip about an inch of insulation from the wire extending from the loop. This completes the loop.

## Making the Variable Capacitor

1. With the scissors, cut two strips of aluminum foil about 8 inches wide and 12 inch long (the width of the Reynolds wrap).

2. Insert each aluminum strip in a plastic paper protector. An inch or so of foil should extend beyond the protector opening when the foil is fully inserted. Carefully fold this exposed foil several times to form a neat ridge at the edge of the protector. This ridge will later be used for making electrical connections.

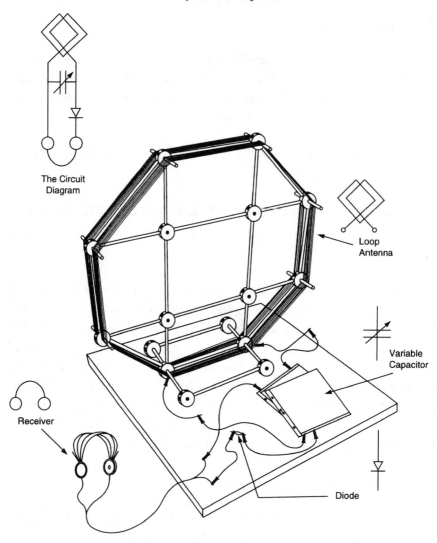

The Circuit Diagram

Loop Antenna

Variable Capacitor

Receiver

Diode

Figure 1: Low budget xtal set

3. Put the two foil lined paper protectors together to meet three conditions (see Figure 1):

> Condition 1.  The 3 holes of each protector are to your left side.

Condition 2. The exposed foil ridge on the bottom protector is at the top (furthest from you).

Condition 3. The exposed foil ridge on the top protector is at the bottom (closest to you).

4. Insert the round-head paper fastener from the bottom through the center holes of the protectors and fold the prongs over gently. The protectors must turn relative to one another about this center fastener.

5. Locate the assembly to your right and secure the bottom protector to the table top with scotch tape. This completes our variable capacitor.

## Interconnecting the Components

1. Using test leads, connect one end of a test lead to the exposed copper at the end of the loop wire fastened at the right base of the coil. Connect the clip at the other end of this test lead to the roll of aluminum foil at the top of the variable capacitor (bottom protector).

2. Connect one end of another test lead to the exposed copper at the end of the loop wire fastened at the left base of the coil. Connect the other end of this test lead to the roll of aluminum foil at the bottom of the variable capacitor (top protector).

3. Connect the right side of the loop to one side of the receiver (earphone).

4. Connect the other side of the receiver to one end of the 1N34A diode.

5. Connect the free end of the 1N34A diode to the left side of the loop.

This completes the wiring of the set.

## Operating the Set

1. Estimate the direction to a local AM radio transmitter. Align the loop such that one end is closest to that station and the other end is furthest from that station. This should give the best reception (see below).

2. Starting with the protectors aligned one on top of the other, place a book or magazine over the protectors to hold the foil "plates" close together. Then slowly rotate the top protector about the mounting fastener while listening to the receiver. Tune for maximum signal strength.

Once a signal is received, its volume can be changed by rotating the loop about its vertical axis. Indeed, when looking through the loop, in a direction normal to the plane of the loop, either directly toward or directly away from the transmitting station, the signal goes to zero. This is called a null and it is useful in radio direction finding.

## Conclusion

If the set you built works, then you have succeeded in capturing a narrow band of radio-frequency energy using two physical phenomena. First, a signal voltage was induced by a changing magnetic field linking the wire turns in the loop. Second, the electrical signal was enhanced by electrical resonance when the capacitor was adjusted to resonate with the loop inductance. You recovered the audio signal from the high frequency voltage whose amplitude varied in accordance with that audio frequency. You did this by rectifying the high frequency signal with the crystal diode (see the Introduction of this book for more details). You converted that audio voltage to audible sound with the receiver. In summary, you built a functional radio powered only by a small part of the radiation energy that surrounds us.

If your success in building a crystal radio sparks your interest in learning more about technical things, then welcome to the beautiful world of mathematics and physics. It's a world uncluttered by opinion and conjecture. It's a world of unlimited learning opportunity, both of things known and of things yet to be discovered.

## About the Author

Bill and Elaine Simes live in Overland Park, Kansas, 70 miles or so from the small town where Bill grew up. Stored in their basement, together with shop equipment and apparent trappings from a physics museum, is a set of the 1933 World Book Encyclopedia. Even on the closed Vol. 14, a band of discolored pages explaining radio of that era give silent testimony to Bill's early interests. His uncle and early mentor was Ray Moler, chief engineer of what was then KMBC in Kansas City. Ray instilled in Bill an early interest in things electronic. On family visits, Ray sometimes brought Bill old radio parts which were treasures to the young enthusiast. In his senior high school year, Bill ran a radio repair shop on Saturdays and evenings after school. During WWII he served as an Aviation Electronics Technician in the navy. After the war he earned his BSEE from the University of Missouri then his MSEE from the University of Kansas. He has worked for Philco as a technical advisor to the Air Force and for Bendix as an engineering supervisor. Bill is now retired, but he retains his pilot license, his radio amateur license, (WØIZC), and his professional Missouri engineering registration. Bill's proudest accomplishment in life was to father a nuclear engineer, now a full-time mother to the 5 grandkids.

This is the first of three wonderful projects by Mr. Simes. The other two, found in later chapters, are "A Krystal Kludge" and "Yesterday's Circuit Today's Parts."

# A Loop Antenna Crystal Set
by Michael Mauser

This loop antenna crystal set is one I designed for a class I taught for 12 year olds. I wanted to build a set that would not require a ground or external antenna, which was cheap, and which could be assembled by young children without requiring too many tools. This design worked well. I just had to prepare the wood parts ahead of time. We also experimented with an outside antenna, adding speakers, and using galena crystals with a fine piece of wire held in place with a clothes pin for a detector. We were fortunate that we were fairly close to a 1,000 watt AM station, but I think many experimenters will also be close enough to powerful stations to be successful. These are not terribly sensitive sets, but my emphasis was on something simple and cheap. This would give the kids an opportunity to learn and also feel they were doing more than just putting a kit together. The set has the advantages of being easy to build, cheap, portable, and highly directional. You can also amplify the signal from it or connect it to a regular antenna and ground for an increase in sensitivity.

## Building the Set

This set consists of a loop antenna, a tuning capacitor, a germanium diode detector and a high impedance earphone. Each of these parts are described below. Before starting, check Table 1 to make sure you have all the parts, supplies and tools you need. Also, read through the instructions so you know what substitutions you can make.

## Loop Antenna

We will make the loop antenna about 1 foot across with 15 turns. This size is manageable and doesn't use much wire. Later, you can try using a larger loop or you can add another antenna, using the original loop antenna as a tuning coil.

Cut out a 11½ by 18 inch piece of 3/4-inch plywood. Measure down 11½ inches along the 18-inch sides and draw a line across the board. Draw diagonal lines from each of the top corners of the plywood to the ends of the line you just drew. Measure 4 inches in along the diagonals and draw a circle or square. Finally cut out the circle or square as shown in Figure 1. This hole is optional, but it makes it easier to attach the arms and makes the completed set easier to carry.

Drill thirteen 1/8-inch holes as shown in Figure 1. Eight of the holes are for screws to attach the arms for the wire, three holes are for the

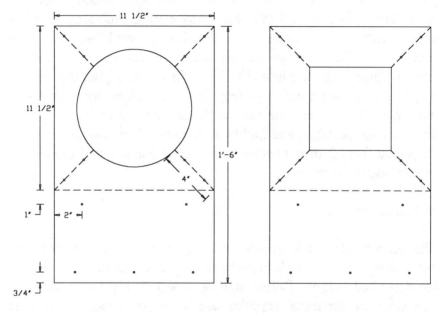

base, and two holes are for the wire that will be wound on the arms.

Figure 1: Hole layout for plywood frame (use either pattern)

Cut four 4-inch long pieces of very dry 2x4 redwood. These will be the arms. We want the wood dry so it doesn't conduct electricity. We use redwood because it is soft, but you can use another type of wood if you want. You can also use 1x4 wood, but if you do, you

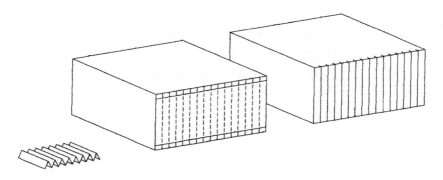

Figure 2: Marking and notching arms for wire

may want to predrill the holes for the screws so they don't split the wood.

We need to cut 15 slots 1/8-inch deep in one end of each of the four pieces of 2x4 for the wire. But first cut out a 1¾ inch-wide by 3½ inch-long piece of paper. Fold the paper in half, then fold each half in half, then each quarter in half, and finally each eighth in half. Refold the paper to make an accordion as shown in Figure 2. Now lay the paper across the end of a 2x4 and use a pencil to mark lines on both ends of each fold so that you have 15 marks on each side of the paper. Finally, line up a hacksaw on these marks and saw the slots. (You may need to use a bigger saw if you use wire bigger than 22 gauge.)

Now lay the 2x4 pieces on a work bench or the floor with the slotted ends facing out (arrange the arms so that they will be attached as shown in Figure 3). Set the plywood frame on top of them and adjust the 2x4s so they are centered over the diagonal lines and screw them on. I used No. 6 x 1 5/8-inch phosphate sheet rock screws because they are cheap and have a Phillips type head which makes them easy to screw, but you can use other types of wood screws if you like. You may want to drill pilot holes first to make it easier to screw, or you can use a screw gun or chuck a screw bit in a variable speed drill.

To complete the frame, screw an 11½ inch long piece of 2x6 redwood to the bottom of the plywood. If you extend the plywood a tiny ways past the edge of the 2x6, when the frame sits upright it will rest on the edge of the plywood and may be more stable. It should look like Figure 3 when it is upright.

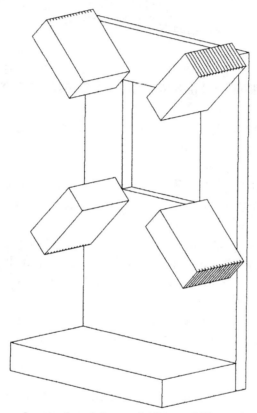

Figure 3: View of completed frame before adding wire

Next comes the wire. I used a 75-foot roll of 26-gauge magnet wire. Magnet wire is solid copper wire with an enamel coating for insulation. You can get this from Radio Shack in a package along with a 40-foot roll of 22-gauge magnet wire and a 200-foot roll of 30-gauge magnet wire. You can use the other wire for antennas and other things later. You can also buy a 100-foot roll of 22, 24, or 26-gauge magnet wire. You can even unwind magnet wire from an old solenoid or motor. You don't even have to use magnet wire.

Magnet wire is cheap and easy to work with, but you can use stranded or solid core insulated or insulated wire also. You don't want to use wire too small in diameter because the resistance will be greater, and you don't want wire too thick either because it is more expensive and it may be hard to bend.

Push about 2 feet of wire—the length doesn't need to be exact—through the left lower hole in the frame and staple or thumbtack it to the back of the plywood. Now start winding the coil clockwise starting in the first slot of the bottom left 2x4 (refer to Figure 4).

Connection tags are added to the loops to allow experimenting with connections and to allow an external antenna or ground to be added later for improved reception. They are not required but are highly recommended. Every 2 or 3 turns, make a connection tag along the bottom part of the loop by scraping or otherwise removing the insulation on a 1-inch long portion of the wire and then twisting it so the uninsulated part hangs down. Make your first connection tag on one end and the next one slightly over as you wind the antenna so they are nicely spaced along the bottom. If you run out of room, just start again on the same end and start a second row of connection tags. The exact number and position of these is not important. After you finish the last loop, cut the wire after leaving about 2 feet, and thread the end through the second hole in the plywood. Staple or thumbtack the wire to the back of the plywood.

## Tuning Capacitor

We will use aluminum foil and wax paper to make a tuning capacitor. A capacitor is just two electrical conductors separated by electrical insulation. The larger the area of the conductors and the thinner the insulation separating them, the larger the capacitance. A tuning capacitor (or variable capacitor) is a capacitor that can be adjusted, either by changing the area of the conductors or the distance between them. We will use a design that will keep us from having to attach a wire to the moving part.

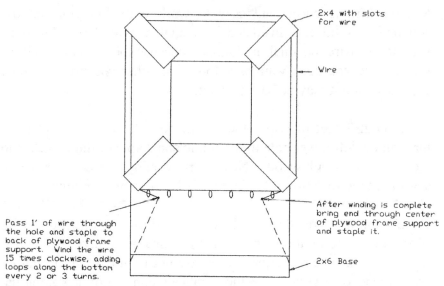

Figure 4: View of wire added to frame

Cut out two pieces of aluminum foil, each 3½ by 6½ inches. Lay these pieces on the 2x6 base of the frame antenna so they are up against the plywood and they are close to each other but not touching, maybe about ¾-inch apart (see Figure 5). Now fold down the ends that overhang the ends of the 2x6 base; these should be about 1 inch long. Use a couple of staples or thumbtacks on the folded down part and a little tape along the top to hold the aluminum foil in place.

Now attach the wires from the loop antenna. Bring the start of the antenna wire (the piece that went through the left side 1/8 inch hole as you face the antenna) around to the side of the 2x6 base. You may want to cut a little slot in the edge of the plywood where the wire makes the bend to keep the wire in place. Be careful to keep the wire low enough down so you can slide the movable part of the tuning capacitor freely on the 2x6 base without snagging the wire. Now scrape the enamel insulation off the wire, being careful to get down to bright copper. Lay the uninsulated bare wire against the folded down strip of aluminum foil and staple or thumbtack it in place. Cut off extra wire, but leave a short piece of wire sticking out away from the aluminum foil. We will connect the earphone to this short piece.

Prepare and connect the wire on the right hand side in the same way, again leaving a short piece of wire sticking out away from the aluminum foil for attaching to the diode detector.

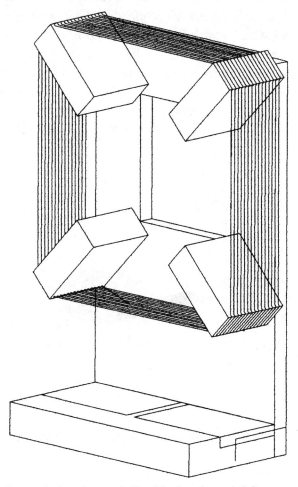

Figure 5: View of aluminum foil added to base of frame

Finally, take an 11½-inch piece of 2x4 and lay a piece of aluminum foil 6 by 6 inches in the center and fold the edges of the aluminum foil down. You can staple or thumbtack the edges to the 2x4 if you wish, but it is not absolutely needed. Now lay a piece of wax paper over the tinfoil and fold the wax paper down over the sides of the 2x4 and tape it in place. Lay the wrapped 2x4 with the aluminum foil side down on top of the aluminum foil on the 2x6 base as shown in Figure 6. (This actually forms two capacitors in series—the aluminum foil on the left side of the base forms a capacitor with the aluminum foil on the 2x4 block which overlays it, and the aluminum foil on the right side forms a second capacitor with the aluminum foil on the 2x4 which overlays it. We could have left off one of the two pieces of aluminum foil on the base, but then we would have to attach a wire to the aluminum foil on the 2x4 block.)

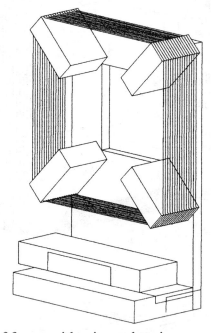

Figure 6: View of frame with wire and tuning capacitor

## Diode Detector

Crystal detectors are the forerunners of modern semiconductor devices. The simplest semiconductor devices are diodes and transistors. We will use a diode for the detector because, unlike a crystal detector, it requires no adjustment. We will use a germanium type diode because it has a very low voltage drop, and this means we will have more voltage for the earphones. The most popular germanium diode is the 1N34A, but you can try a 1N64, 1N67. 1N68, 1N95, 1N100, 1N277, 1N295, 1N617, or 1N665. Later, you can make your own detector or substitute other types of diodes or semiconductors. Staple or thumbtack the diode to the 2x6 base in front of the tuning capacitor and bend the leads up.

## High Impedance Earphone

The earphones or headphones you normally use with portable radios, tape players, and CD players are low impedance devices, typically 8 ohms. We need an earphone or headphone with an impedance of 1,000 ohms or more. These are not very common, but you can still get them (see Table 1 and the vendor list at the back of this book). You can use 8 ohm earphones or headphones, or even a small speaker, but then you will need to add an audio transformer which will transform an 8 ohm load to a 1,000 ohm load.

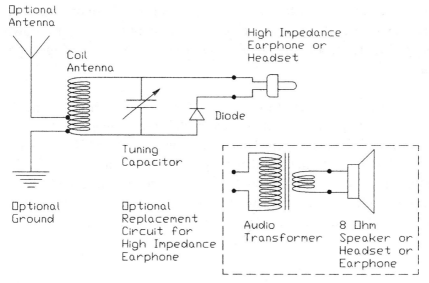

Figure 7: Connection schematic. Note: If a earphone is used rather than headphones, a resistor is required "across" the earphone.

Figure 7 shows how you can substitute an audio transformer you can buy from Radio Shack and an 8-ohm headset or speaker for the harder to find high impedance earphone or headset. If you use a speaker you will have better luck with the ones used with small cassette tape and CD players, and you may also need to hook up an additional antenna or ground for more volume. If you use a high impedance ceramic earphone, connect a 10,000 to 1,000,000 ohm resister in parallel with it for better audio.

## Connecting and Operating the Set

Add alligator clips to the earphone wires and make a jumper by adding alligator clips to both ends of a 2-foot piece of wire. Connect the earphone between one of the capacitor wires and the diode and connect the jumper between the other capacitor wire and the other end of the diode. You can experiment with other connection points later.

To operate your set, orient it so the 2x4 tuning capacitor slide points at a broadcast station, then slide the 2x4 back and forth or raise it up and down to change the capacitance. You may need to push down on the 2x4 to smooth out the aluminum foil and wax paper for more capacitance.

Try connecting a ground to one end of the coil at a connection tab. Try connecting an external antenna at different connection tabs. A good external antenna will be 100 feet or more long, 20 feet high, and pointed toward the broadcast station antenna, but you can get by with a lot less. A good ground could be a second wire laid on the ground directly under the antenna, or it can be a wire attached to a buried metal such as an electrical ground rod. Good luck!

## Table 1: What you need to build this crystal set

*Supplies and Parts*

one 11½ by 18 inch piece of ¾ inch plywood[a]
four 4 inch pieces of 2x4 redwood[b]
eleven number 6 x 1 5/8 inch sheet rock screws or wood screws
one 11½ inch piece of 2x6 redwood
one 11½ inch piece of 2x4 redwood
aluminum foil, wax paper, tape
four screw terminal alligator clips (Radio Shack #270-346 or
    Mouser #13AC008)[c]
80 feet of 26 gauge or larger magnet wire (Radio Shack #278-1345
    or salvage wire from solenoid coil, motor, etc.
Crystal earplug (available from Xtal Set Society),
    or 2000 ohm headset,
    or standard 8 ohm earphone and one audio output
    transformer (RS#33-175 & #273-1380)
IN34A general purpose point contact germanium signal diode
    Radio Shack #276-1123 or Mouser #333-1N34A)

*Suggested Tools*

| | | |
|---|---|---|
| handsaw or electric saw | wire cutters | pocket knife |
| drill with 1/8 inch bit | stapler | scissors |
| hacksaw | needle nose pliers | |
| Phillips screwdriver | straight slot screwdriver | |

*Notes:*

a    other thicknesses of plywood can be used or another
     similar material.
b    Redwood is used because it is soft, but any other soft
     wood will do.  Use dry wood.
c    If you have a soldering iron, you can use the solder
     type alligator clips.

# Benjamin and David Goldenberg's Very-Fine Old-Time Crystal Radio

by Benjamin and David Goldenberg

A few years ago I set out to build a set with my son Benjamin, assuming it would be easy as when I was a boy. I discovered it wasn't! After some fumbling around, the two important lessons I learned were: (1) The importance (and scarcity) of high-impedance earphones and (2) the scarcity of variable capacitors in this digital age. After we had finally succeeded, we thought it would be fun to put together a kit, with parts and instructions, for others.

Table 1: Parts List

| Item | Qty |
|---|---|
| PVC pipe, 1" outside diameter (3/4" size) x 4" | 1 |
| Aluminum or steel sheet metal, 0.5" wide x 5" | 1 |
| Coil wire (#24 magnet wire) | 36 ft |
| Hook-up wire (#22) | 25 ft |
| Crystal earphone | 1 |
| Jack for the earphone plug | 1 |
| Crystal diode (1N34A) | 1 |
| Capacitor, 470 picofarad | 1 |
| #8 sheet metal screws | 8 |
| 8-32 machine screw, 1" long | 1 |
| 8-32 nuts | 2 |
| flat washers | 6 |
| Ring terminal (lug) | 1 |
| Board, 3/4" thick, approximately 7" x 9" | 1 |

What else you will need:

Vise-Grip pliers
Soldering iron and solder
File or motorized grinder
   (e.g. Moto-Tool)

Wire cutters
Drill, with 1/8", 3/16" and 3/8" bits
Screwdriver
Scotch tape

## Contruction of Special Parts

The following steps involve making a few special parts for the radio. Some of these steps are most easily performed using power tools, and some involve soldering. This work should be done by someone old enough and knowledgeable enough to handle these tools safely. Once these parts are made, however, the rest of the project requires only hand tools and can be completed by nearly anyone.

## Coil Form

The coil form is a piece of PVC pipe, 1" in diameter (outside) and 4" long. (For reasons fully understood only by plumbers, pipe of this diameter is referred to as 3/4".) To facilitate mounting the coil to the board, drill two sets of holes on opposite sides of the form, see (see Figure 1). On one side of the form, drill two holes, 3/16" in diameter and 3/8" from each end. Directly opposite from these holes, drill two more holes 3/8" in diameter. Screws will be placed through the smaller holes, while the larger ones make it easy to reach the screws with a screwdriver.

## Slider

Drill two 3/16" holes in the piece of sheet metal, each 1/4" from an end. After the holes are drilled, place a bend in the metal 3/4" from each end, as shown in the Figure 2. Use a vise or pliers to bend the metal. Use a file to smooth all of the edges and corners of the metal.

CAUTION: Drilling sheet metal can be very dangerous! If the bit catches on the metal, you can have a very sharp edge flying through your hands. Hold the metal firmly with a pair of pliers (preferably Vise-Grip type), not with your hands! Also, place a piece of wood under the metal as you drill. This will help keep the metal from tearing and grabbing the bit as it passes through.

## Pointed Screw for Slider

Using either a file or a grinder, grind a point on the 8-32 machine screw. The point doesn't need to be very sharp; about like the tip of a medium ball-point pen is ideal.

## Earphone Jack with Wires

Cut two pieces of hook-up wire 2" long. Remove 1/4" of insulation form one end of each wire and solder the wires to the terminals of the earphone jack. Remove 1/2" of insulation from the other ends of the wires.

Note: Headphone jacks often have more than two terminals. Make sure that the terminals you solder to are the ones that will be connected to the tip and side of the plug when it is inserted.

## Ring Terminal with Two Wires

Cut two pieces of hook-up wire, one 7" long and the other 2". Remove 1/4" of insulation from one end of each wire. Solder the two wires to the ring terminal. Remove 1/2" of insulation from the other ends of the wires.

## Board

Tape the layout template to a board, approximately 7" x 9", and drill a 1/8" hole at each position marked with a cross. Make sure that holes B and C can be aligned with the 3/8" holes on the PVC coil form before proceeding. (The layout template is on the last page of this project. Use a photocopier to enlarge the template by 52% to fit the 7" x 9" board and coil form.)

## Assembly

### Wind the Coil

The coil is made by wrapping the #24 magnet wire onto the coil form, which is made from a piece of PVC pipe. The magnet wire is the wire that looks like it has no insulation on it. But, it is actually coated with a thin layer of enamel. This coating must be removed from the ends of the wire before making any connections.

The best way to wind the coil is with two people, one to hold the wire taut (the holder) and the other to wind it onto the coil form (the wrapper). First, thread the end of the coil wire from the outside of the form through one of the large holes and out the end of the form. Leave about 4" of wire going out the end. Hold onto the other end of the wire and begin wrapping it around the form, starting right next to the hole. After you have wound a few turns on, push the wire together so it is nice and neat and put a piece of Scotch tape over it. The coil should look like this:

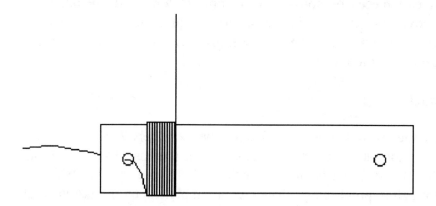

Figure 1: Preparing the coil

Now, the "holder" should hold the spool of wire loosely while the "wrapper" walks across the room unwinding the wire. Then, the holder should hold the spool very tightly so that the wrapper can wind the wire onto the pipe evenly. Each turn should be wrapped on right next to the previous turn, but shouldn't overlap. As the wire is wrapped on, the wrapper slowly walks across the room keeping the wire tight. When the wrapper reaches the holder, hold the wire that has been wrapped onto the form tightly, while the holder lets the wire on the spool unwrap. The wrapper then walks back across the room unwinding the wire from the spool, and the same procedure is repeated.

When the coil is within about 1/8" of the holes at the other end of the coil, stop winding. Put a piece of Scotch tape on the end of the wrapping, and cut the wire a few inches from the end of the coil. Thread the end of the wire through the large hole in the form.

### Attach the Coil to the Board

Use two of the #8 sheet metal screws to attach the coil to the board, using holes B and C that you drilled. Place the screws through the small holes in the coil form from the inside. You can then use the large holes on the other side of the form to reach the screws with a screwdriver. Make sure the coil is attached snugly to the board.

### Assemble the Slider

Find the slider, the 8-32 screw and the two 8-32 nuts. Thread one of the nuts onto the screw until it is about 3/8" from the head of the screw. Put the screw through one of the holes in the slider and thread the other nut on, so that the slider looks like this from the side:

Figure 2: Slider assembly

Tighten the second nut against the slider and the first nut with a wrench.

## Attach the Slider to the Board

Find a sheet metal screw, a washer and the ring terminal with two wires attached to it. Put the screw through the ring terminal, then through the washer, and finally through the open hole in the slider assembly (from the top of the slider as shown in Figure 2). Attach the entire assembly to the board with the screw at hole E. Tighten the screw so that it is snug but still allows the slider to move back and forth. The pointed end of the machine screw at the other end of the slider should press firmly against the wire on the coil. If necessary bend the slider so that it makes firm contact with the coil but can still move.

Move the slider back and forth on the coil to scrape the enamel insulation from the coil wire where the pointed end of the machine screw touches it. Or you can use the slider gently to mark the path, and then follow-up with sandpaper. The screw should be able to make an electrical contact with the coil wire at any position along the length of the coil.

## Put the Remaining Screws in the Board

Screw the remaining sheet metal screws into holes A, D, F, G and H, with a washer on each screw. Do not tighten the screws yet.

## Wire the Components of the Radio Together

Use the circuit drawing in Figure 3 as a guide. For each connection, make sure that the insulation is removed from the end of the wire. Wrap the bare ends of the wires around the screw between the screw head and the washer underneath.

a. Wrap the two wires from the earphone jack around screws F and H. Do not tighten these screws yet.

b. Take the short wire from the slider and wrap the bare end around screw F (which should already be attached to one of the earphone jack wires). Do not tighten the screw yet.

c. Take the long wire from the slider and wrap the bare end around screw A. Do not tighten this screw yet.

d. Find the crystal diode, the small cylinder with two bare wires attached to it. Wrap one of the wires around screw H (attached to the other earphone jack wire), and tighten the screw.

e. Take the other wire from the diode and wrap it around screw G. Do not tighten this screw yet.

f. Find the capacitor, the small disc with two bare wires attached to it. Wrap one of the wires around screw F and tighten the screw.

g. Wrap the other wire from the capacitor around screw G, but do not tighten this screw yet.

h. Cut a piece of hook-up wire about 6" long and remove about 1/2" of insulation from each end. Wrap one end around screw G and tighten the screw. Wrap the other end of the wire around screw D, but do not tighten this screw yet.

i. Take the wire from the right hand end of the coil and remove the insulation from about 1/2" from the end of the wire. To remove the insulation, either lightly scrape the wire with a knife or use a small piece of sandpaper. Wrap the bare end of the wire around screw D, but do not tighten the screw yet.

## Connect the Radio to Ground

In order to work, the crystal radio must be wired to a good ground connection. Often, the easiest way to make a ground connection is to use the grounding circuit for the house's electrical system. Cut a piece of hook-up wire long enough to reach from the radio to a nearby electrical outlet. Remove 1/2" of insulation from each end of the wire. Wrap one end around screw A of the radio and tighten the screw. On the electrical outlet, loosen the screw that holds the plate on the box. Wrap the other end of the wire around this screw and tighten it.

CAUTION: Be sure not to let the wire or anything else touch the 120 V socket!

Alternatively, you can use a cold water pipe to connect the radio to ground. Remove a few inches of insulation from the wire from screw A of the radio and wrap the bare end tightly around a cold water pipe. Another way to do this which works even better is to buy a ground clamp for your size pipe from an electrical store. Be sure to thoroughly remove paint from the pipe before installing the clamp.

## Connect an Antenna to the Radio

Use the rest of the hook-up wire to make an antenna. Remove 1/2" of insulation from one end of the wire and wrap it around screw D. Tighten the screw. Unwind the wire from the spool and try to place it as high as possible in the room.

In areas with many powerful radio stations nearby, an inside antenna should be adequate to receive a few stations. If you have trouble hearing anything, it may help to set up a long outside antenna. Radio Shack sells a kit with the necessary wire and other parts (cat. no. 278-758).

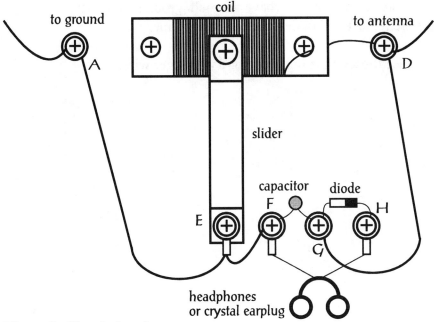

Figure 3: Circuit drawing

## Try the Radio!

Plug the earphone into the jack. Listen to the earphone and slowly move the slider across the coil. Try to find the position where a station is loudest. You should be able to hear a few different stations with the slider at different positions.

## If the Radio Doesn't Work, Check the Following:

a. Make sure all of the connections are correct and that the insulation has been removed from the wires where they are wrapped around screws. Also check that there aren't any short circuits between the screws or bare wires.

b. Make sure that you scraped the insulation from the coil wire with the slider so that the slider can make good contact with the coil.

c. Make sure that you have a good ground connection.  Try a different electrical outlet or a cold water pipe.

d. Place the antenna higher up or try a longer wire.

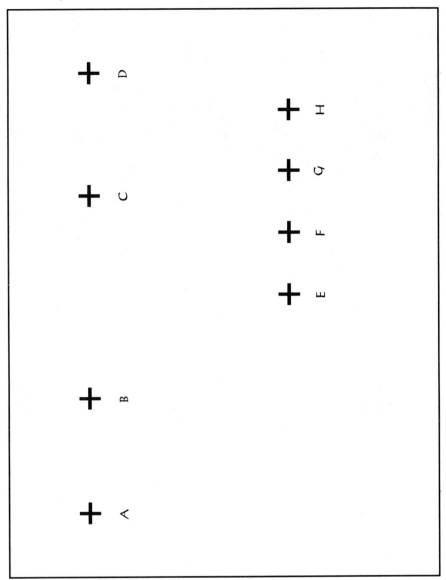

Figure 4: Layout Template

# The Directional Loop DX Xtal Set
By Joseph Cooper

## Introduction to the Directional Loop Xtal Set Project

The directional loop crystal set is an attempt to move beyond some of the limitations found in the classical crystal set design of a coil/capacitor (L/C) tank circuit attached to a dipole antenna. By borrowing the best of current ideas and past designs it is hoped that the resulting hybrid will help many people realize a new potential in crystal set design. It is also hoped that many may re-capture some of the excitement and fascination of crystal radio by being able to pull in distant (DX) stations with greater frequency and ease.

## The Design Project

The Diamond DX Xtal set did not come about due to a systematic or scientific attempt at design. It was a case of an "Ah Ha!" occurring after several months of reading a variety of topics about radio while having the need for a new crystal set design lurking in the back of my mind. The reason for this need was a growing sense of personal frustration when working with traditional crystal radio set designs.

The primary way to improve crystal set design has been through the addition of something to the basic circuit. Most often experimenters increase the length or height of the antenna, add more coils and capacitors, and use signal amplification, particularly of the audio. These are all fine in themselves and can produce the required results, but often at the expense of the basic simplicity of the original design. Is there a better way to design a crystal set in order to produce the level of performance desired without making the set complicated to operate or requiring a large antenna array?

With this in mind, the design of an improved crystal set was embarked upon. The following points were important clues for such an improvement:

A) Radio waves in the frequency range of the broadcast band (530-1710 Khz) are affected not only by the reflective property of the ionosphere, but also the ground, water, and air surfaces over which it travels.

B) BCB (broadcast band) radio waves are generated by vertical antennas and are thus vertically polarized when they leave those antennas, but this will be modified by effects of A (above).

C) In general, when BCB radio waves arrive at a distant reception site they are no longer vertical, but are tilted in several directions.

D) The strength of the signal will always be greatest from the point of the broadcast.

and finally,

E) A though D are complicated by the fact that with BCB radio wave propagation there will always be some mixture of ground wave (signals that travel along the surface of the earth) and sky wave (signals that bounce off the reflective ionosphere layer of the atmosphere) signals.

The solution for the above conditions that is applied in conventional radio design for BCB and Low Frequency use has been to use the loop antenna. This type of antenna has many virtues that make it ideal; it is small and compact, while being able to capture radio signals with close to the same strength as strung wire antennas such as the dipole or long wire. A further advantage with the loop is that it actually reduces natural radio noise, rather than increasing it as is found in the case of the vertical antenna. The most notable and desirable characteristic for the loop, and which it is most often utilized for, is its ability to be highly directional. It can "null" or neutralize signals that may be on or near the same frequency being tuned.

One particular loop design that is popular amongst BCB DXers in Canada and Britain is the foundation for this project[1]. This loop design uses a simple L/C device that couples to an existing ferrite loop antenna as is found in many of today's transistor BCB radios. By placing the external loop near such a radio when it is tuned to a weak station, and by using a 365 pf tuning capacitor that is attached to the external loop, the coupled circuit will increase the effectiveness of the radio's own antenna circuit. By pointing both directly at the weak station, the signal strength will be further increased, while nulling any other stations that are on the same frequency, but not directly in line with the antennas.

## Building the Loop Crystal Set

The design of the loop crystal set presented here is not absolute, but can be the foundation for much experimentation. In general the aim here is to show the most simplest design, and one that needs only a minimum of tools, if any.

A project could be constructed entirely of pre-cut and sanded wood that is available from many hobby, hardware or building supply locations, and which is glued together. Likewise it is possible to simply build the loop using either the wood cross arms, or even a cardboard box, and then purchasing a plastic "Lazy Susan" (rotating) tray to place is upon. The key here is to use your imagination and improve upon the design as need dictates.

A) Begin with the construction of the wooden cross arms for the loop.

Note: A parts and source list is provided at the end of this project.

1) If tools are available, cut a notch into the center of two pieces 18 inches long by 1 1/2 inches wide by 1/4 to 1/2 inches deep wood board. The notches should be equal to 1/2 the width, and accommodate the depth. The result should be a snug fit between

the center notches on the two boards, forming an X shape. The board, can be glued for further strength.

2) If tools are not available, attach two short pieces of wood (each a bit less than 9 inches) with a single long piece (18 inches) with two short. Try to have the lengths of the short pieces be such as to keep the symmetry of the cross arms (to keep the loop square).

B) Wrap the wire onto the loop.

1) If tools are available you should drill two holes in one of the arms in order to anchor the beginning and the end of the wire. Likewise is helps to have the ends of the arms notched so as to keep the loops from falling off of the arms as it is being wound.

2) Instead of using tools you can attach double sided tape to the ends of each arm in order to secure the wire as it is being wrapped on. If this is not available, you may place some "white" or carpenters glue on the ends, which is then allowed to become tacky, over which the wire is then wrapped. When the glue is dry it will help keep the wire to remain anchored to the arms.

C) Attach the tuning capacitor to the loop

Note: Before beginning this step it may be necessary (depending on the design of the capacitor) to remove a set of screws that hold components used for fine tuning (which should also be completely removed). This step will allow you to be able to tune through the entire frequency range of the BCB, but it is optional.

Attach the capacitor to one of the arms of the loop by using epoxy glue. Use rubber bands to hold the capacitor to the arm while the epoxy is curing, but be certain to have all of the plates closed and protected during the procedure. You must also remember to place it near the center of the axis, otherwise the loop will tend to be unstable, even when it is attached to the base.

Give the epoxy 24 hours to cure (even for 5 minute type) and then solder the two wires of the loop to the capacitor. Remember to attach one wire to a lug of the stationary plates, and the other to the lug (generally the grounding case) of the rotating plates.

D) Testing the loop

It is wise to see if the loop actually works before proceeding to add the crystal diode and the base. At this point it is easier to re-wire the loop, or fix the capacitor, than at a later stage.

The test requires that you have a simple transistor type BCB radio that has a built-in ferrite antenna (not a telescoping type). Simply turn on the radio and tune in a station at the low end of the dial (around 550 Khz) and place the loop beside the set. Turn the tuning capacitor rotator until you hear a change in the signal strength of the station heard. This will indicate that the loop is working. You should then tune to a station in the high end of the band (above 1500 hz) and tune the loop capacitor again. You should have the same results.

If you do not find that any effect is taking place, check the wire, capacitor and solder joints to see if any problems can be found. Likewise try running the test on a different radio if one is available.

E) Making the base

Note: An easy to find source of pre-made bases for those who do not have access to tools are trophy bases or wood burning plaques. These are inexpensive, come in different sizes, and are available at many hobby or hardware stores.

1) Begin by attaching the Lazy Susan mechanism to the block of wood that will be the stationary base. You can either use epoxy to glue the mechanism to the block or use screws if desired. The important consideration here is ensuring that the turning

mechanism is centered properly so that the antenna portion will rotate with ease.

2) When the base is completed, attach the upper turning base to the upper rotation mechanism by either using epoxy or screws. Take your time to ensure that the upper unit turns true and that the axis is centered properly.

F) Attaching the loop to the base

Note: to perform the following steps properly, ensure that all positions are correctly laid out first. Take your time and follow the rule of "measure twice, and attach once." What is required is very simple; attach two support legs to the loop and then glue the two legs to the rotatable base. If it is not done well, e.g. with the loop being centered over the turning axis of the base correctly, the unit may tend to tip over or be difficult to track through the turning radius.

For the first steps have a ruler and a soft lead pencil available, and for the later have glue and optional screws available.

1) Take two support legs and by hand hold them against one of the support arms of the loop.

2) Place the legs on a flat surface, or on the rotating base, and after ensuring that the loop and the legs are even, mark the upper location of the legs on the arm with the pencil.

3) Glue the legs to the arm, and use elastic bands (or any other firm clamping device) to hold them until the glue is dry. You may also use screws if an even firmer hold is desired.

(Note: as an alternative, if you have the tools available, you may wish to not glue or permanently secure the legs to the arm, but to use removable bolts and wingnuts. The legs would be secured to the base only, and this would allow the loop and the base to be separated for storage or easier transportation.)

4) While the glue is drying, lay out the position for the legs on the rotating base. Establish where the axis of the turn is (which may not be in the exact center of the base due to construction flaws and design problems in the Lazy Susan mechanism). Take some time to simply observe the turning character of the base and work out the approximate axis. From that point begin to measure out the outer and inner distance from that center to the approximate location of the two support legs. Mark these locations lightly using the pencil.

5) When the glue (step F3) is dry, place the legs on the base in the locations where they are to be attached, and see how the unit balances. Try a few turns of the unit in this way as well in order to see how the unit performs. When all appears satisfactory, mark the final location of the legs using the pencil. Remove all other marks at this time.

6) Glue the legs to their permanent location, and use elastic bands to hold the loop and legs against the base. Allow the assembly to dry for at least 24 hours.

G) Final Touches

At this point you now attach the crystal diode to the tuning capacitor, but before you do be certain to:

1) Attach a wooden or plastic tuning knob to the rotor shaft of the capacitor. This is needed in order to isolate the capacitor from the small but noticeable capacitor effect that your hand may have while tuning.

2) Attach either rubber feet or a non-slip material to the lower part of the rotating base.

To connect the diode circuit to the tuning capacitor (see Figure 1):

1) If available, attach a two unit soldering lug to the arm of the loop near the tuning capacitor. This is useful, though not completely necessary for attaching the wires used for the headset/audio amplifier to the crystal.

2) Solder or firmly attach a wire to the base (which is attached to the adjustable plates) of the tuning capacitor. This will be the ground or negative side of the circuit.

3) Solder or firmly attach the crystal diode to the free lug of the stationary rotors that is on the opposite side of the lug that is attached to the loop of the antenna. (I mention this so that if you have a dual ganged capacitor, you do not use the unused side.) This is the "positive" side of the circuit so be certain that the wire from the black polarity indication band side of the crystal diode is not used here.

4) Attach (but do not solder) the negative wire from the tuning capacitor to one soldering lug and the positive wire from the crystal to the other. Then attach the wires for either the socket or the plug for the headphones/audio amplifier to the solder lugs, being certain to observe the proper polarity as well, and again do not solder.

5) Connect a .001 microfarad (μfd) capacitor across the soldering lugs and solder all joints.

## Using the Loop Antenna Crystal Set

The operation of the loop antenna crystal set is very easy; simply connect headphones to the unit and then aim the loop in the direction you wish to receive signals from while tuning. You should quickly hear a number of local stations.

To test the directional ability of the loop, simply tune in a station that is about medium strength and turn the loop. You should hear the station drop in strength when the loop is broadside to the direction of the station. You should also find that as you continue to turn the loop the strength will increase as the back of the loop is pointed at the station.

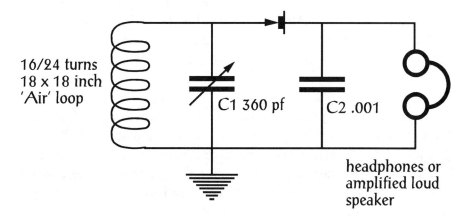

Figure 1: Schematic

To fully take advantage of the directional ability of the loop, work out by using a compass and a map where the points of the compass are at your receiving location, and where key cities or stations are located. One word of note here; don't use the compass near the loop! As an interesting experiment, setup the loop and compass together and tune the loop with the capacitor. You should see the compass needle move as the loop creates its own magnetic field.

To dramatically demonstrate to yourself the DX capability and directional effect of the loop, begin listening with the set just before sunset and point it to the south. Then move the direction of the loop to the west if you live near the east coast or central states, or to the east if you live in the west, as the sunset progresses. You should be able to track the opening of the DX as new stations begin to appear at tuning spots where none were heard before.

What is the most exciting part of using the loop is being able to separate several stations on the same frequency by turning the loop. Loud stations that once covered up weaker ones can be nulled out and weak stations can be strengthened by pointing the loop at them. You may be able to hear many clear channel stations that have a frequency all to themselves which are hundreds of miles away.
The portability of the set also allows you to go to quiet locations in the country, or even in different parts of a city. It would be interesting to try trans-Atlantic or trans-Pacific DX by setting up the unit right beside the ocean. By not having to string a long wire antenna, or even using a ground, you are no longer limited to a permanent location.

Do not forget that the loop can be used as a passive coupled antenna with an existing BCB radio that has a ferrite loop antenna. The use of the loop will significantly improve reception of both local and DX stations. Just tune in a desired station, place the loop near to the radio, and then tune the loop itself. You will hear the signal strength improve if the loop is coupling properly.

[1]A special thanks to Jack Henshaw and Phil Gebhardt of the Ontario DX Association for providing this information.

## Parts List

| Qty | Part | Suggested Supplier | Part or Part Number |
|---|---|---|---|
| Electronics | | | |
| 65 ft | 22 Gauge Stranded Hookup wire | Radio Shack | 278-1296 |
| 1 | Germanium Diode 1N34A | Radio Shack | 276-1123 |
| 1 | .001 µf disk capacitor | Radio Shack | 272-126* |
| 1 | 360 pf variable capacitor | Xtal Set Soc | 365 |
| 1 | single lug solder post | | |
| 1 | headphones or earplug | | |
| 1 | dual lug solder post | | |
| | | | |
| Hardware | | | |
| 1 | Lazy Susan 3.5in | | |
| 4 | self sticking rubber feet | | |
| 2 | ¼ in wood screws | | Optional |
| | | | |
| Wood | | | |
| 1 | 18" x 1.75" x .5" | | |
| 2 | 8.5" x 1.75" x .5" | | see note✦ |
| 2 | 6" x 2" x .75" | | the legs |
| | | | |
| Hobby Supply | | | |
| 2 | 6" Wood Burning Disk | | Base |
| 1 | 2" Wood Toy Wheel | | Knob on cap |
| 1 | 5 Minute Epoxy | | |

*Note: the package will say 1000pf, which is equivalent
✦If you have tools and can notch the arms—use two 18" lengths

# Bibliography

Cooke, B.W "Radio Wave Radiation and Antennas," in <u>Applied Practical Radio-Television,</u> Coyne Radio School, 1947.

Gebhardt, Philip "Here's How to design the best beginners' MW Loop" in <u>The Canadian Amateur Magazine</u>, Vol. 24, No. 9, October 1996, pp. 41-43.

Gebhardt, Philip "January Loop Party," in <u>DX Ontario</u>, Vol. 22, Edition 246, March 1996, pp. 11-12.

Kendall, Jr., Lewis F. and Koehler, Robert Philip "Amplifiers, Speakers and Loops" in <u>Radio Simplified: What it is—How to Build and Operate the Apparatus</u>, The John C. Winston Company, 1925.

Jordan, Edward C. "Electromagnetic Waves," in <u>Fundamentals of Radio</u>, Prentice-Hall Inc., 1942.

Lankford, Dallas "Loop Antennas: Theory and Practice," in <u>NRC Loop Antennas—Design and Theory Book</u>, (date unknown).

Staff, "Looking at Loops," Radio Netherland Wereldomroep, 1987.

Trauffer, Arthur "Loop Crystal Set," in <u>Radio and TV Experimenter</u>, Vol. 2, 1952.

# The Den Two Crystal Radio
by Alan Klase

This project originated during my term as Cub Scout Den Leader. I wanted my guys to enjoy the experience of hearing a radio they had built with their own hands out of common materials. Radio projects have been a part of scouting for a long, long, time.

I had several goals in mind when I did this design. First I wanted the boys to do as much of the assembly as possible, including their own coil. Secondly, the design needed to be reproducible by others, and not require hard to get or expensive components. Finally, the set needed to be a reasonably good performer. We were located in the deep suburbs of Philadelphia, with no strong local stations, so a really simple design would only work with a long antenna. Most parents would want to throw a little wire into a tree or stretch it out in the attic and have the set play.

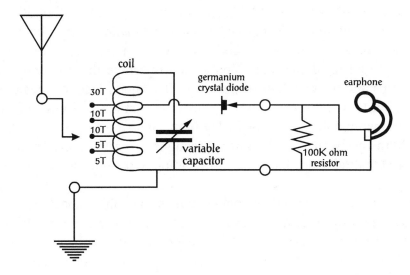

Figure 1: Schematic diagram

The design that emerged, *The Den Two Crystal Radio*, is described as follows. The set is a single tuned parallel circuit consisting of a tapped spider-web coil and a variable capacitor of approximately

365pF maximum capacity (Figure 1). The base of the set is a piece of pine shelving board, and the front panel is 1/4" plywood. The detector, a Radio Shack germanium diode, is connected to the center tap of the 60 turn coil. The coil has three additional taps to accommodate a variety of antennas. Crystal earphones from Mouser Electronics were employed for the headset because of their availability and high performance to cost ratio. A 100K ohm resistor in parallel with the headset provides a DC load for the detector circuit, and avoids the distortion reported by other experimenters.

The spiderweb coil (Figure 2) was chosen because it is easy for young people to wind. Nine-year olds have neither the manual dexterity nor attention span to do a good job of winding a cylindrical coil. The forms were cut from 1/8" Plexiglas using a scroll saw. They should be 4.5 inches in diameter and have nine 1.25 inch radial slots. Similar plastic material is sold in home centers to replace the glass in storm doors. Number 26 enameled "magnet wire" was used. Anything between #24 and #28 should be acceptable. About 60 feet of wire is required. The taps are created by twisting a small eyelet at the appropriate places as the coil is being wound. A crochet hook is a good tool for doing this. You'll need to scrape the insulation off the taps and the two ends of the wire. It's a good idea to spread the taps out to avoid short circuits. Make the first tap at 5 turns (5 full rotations) and the second at 10 1/9 turns, and so on. Be careful that all turns are wound in the same direction. It's easy to get confused when creating a tap, and then start winding in the opposite direction.

The crucial parts are the earphone and the variable capacitor. It is easiest to order the earphones by mail from Mouser; see the vendor list at the back of this book. If you like to use recycled parts you can scrounge around for variable capacitors and knobs. You can purchase 365pF variable capacitors from Antique Electronic Supply also, but it is perfectly acceptable to use a two section capacitor out of a junk clock radio.

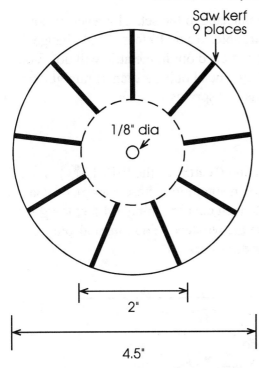

Figure 2: Spiderweb coil form
cut from 1/8" plexiglas or lexan

For the Cub Scouts I spent a couple of months rounding up caps and knobs—talked to the ham radio old timers! I precut and predrilled the coil forms and wooden parts. It's a good idea to chamfer the edges of the coil form slots to avoid scraped insulation. I lucked into a bunch of Fahnstock clips for input and output connections, but binding posts from Radio Shack could be used through the front panel (Figure 3).

I called the Dads in for the meeting when we built the sets. It's a good idea to have a working sample for everyone to copy. I stuck with solder for some of the connections. The kids can at least feed the solder into the joints.

All told, we build eight of these sets. Almost all of them were later set up at home, and everyone was suitably impressed. I was pleased to have had the opportunity to expose young people to radio in this elementary and hands-on way.

Some notes on antenna, ground, and operation for the beginner:

## The Antenna

The ideal crystal set antenna is 75-100 ft of wire, either bare or insulated, erected outdoors in a horizontal direction as high above the ground as humanly possible. An insulated lead-in wire enters under a window sash and is connected to the set. However, is not necessary to go to this much trouble. 30 or 40 feet of light gauge wire strung around a room or stretched out in the attic will do. You might also try clipping onto large metal objects such as rain gutters, etc. (In the real old days it was bed springs.)

## The Ground

The traditional ground connection ("earth" as the British say) is made to a cold-water pipe (use an automotive hose clamp), or to a metal ground rod (a piece of ½ inch copper tubing 3-4 feet long) driven into moist earth outside the window. You might also try connecting to heating pipes or duct work.

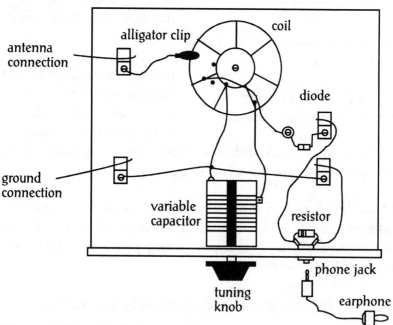

Figure 3: Pictorial diagram of the set

## What Can I Hear?

With a simple antenna you should be able to pick-up your local AM stations. With a better antenna more distant AM stations may come in. At night you'll occasionally hear stations from much further away, and occasionally an international short-wave signal will leak through.

## Operating Instructions

Connect the antenna and ground as in Figure 3. Plug in the earphone. Connect the alligator clip to one of the taps on the coil (see Figure 1). Slowly rotate the tuning knob searching for a station. Try different coil taps and tuning knob positions. The taps closer to the center (ground end) of the coil work best with long antennas, while the higher taps are better with short ones.

## Parts List

| Qty | Description |
| --- | --- |
| 1 | 1/8" small piece of plexiglas |
| 1 | variable capacitor |
| 1 | tuning knob |
| 60ft | #24-#28 enameled wire |
| 1 | crystal earphone |
| 1 | germanium diode |
| 1 | 100K ohm resistor |
| | binding posts |
| | alligator clip |

# How To Build and Use a High Performance Crystal Set

by Lance Borden, WB5REX

One of the most popular serious crystal set circuits to come out of the early days was the double-tuned, tapped-coil unit. One variation was marketed as a kit by Modern Radio Laboratories[1]. There is also a version of this set in K.E. Edwards' book, *Radios that Work for Free.*[2] This set offers good sensitivity, selectivity, and multiple band operation, all in one relatively simple design.

The following is a description of how to build and operate a variation of this circuit using readily available parts and simple construction techniques. With a good antenna system, some practice, and a little patience, this set can receive distant stations on the A.M. band and real DX can be heard from all over the world on the short-wave bands.

## Construction

Begin by acquiring all of the parts and materials you will need before you start. A list of parts is included at the end of this article.

STEP 1. Spray the coil form (an empty toilet paper roll) with one coat of clear acrylic and let it dry. Spray the board (base) with three coats, letting it dry between coats. Shellac can be used instead of acrylic, if you prefer. (Refer to Figure 2 and Photo 3)

STEP 2. Punch two small holes in the coil form 1/4 inch apart and 1/2 inch from one end. Pass 6 inches of the 22 AWG coil wire through one hole from the outside and back through the other. Repeat this process once more and pinch the resulting loops with pliers to secure the coil lead. (Refer to Figure 1)

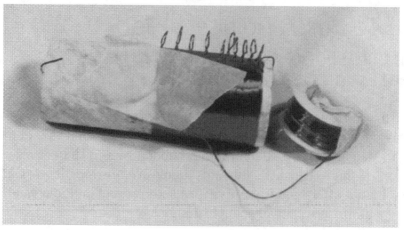

Photo 1: Using tape to hold wire while twisting taps

STEP 3. Wind five turns, close but not overlapping, and make a tap by looping the coil wire around a pencil or other round object. Twist the loop once to secure it and wind five more turns and make another tap. Repeat this process and make additional taps on the following turns: 15, 20, 25, 30, 40, 50, 60, 70, 80, and 90. Punch two holes at the end of the coil form as in step two and secure the end of the coil wire after the 90th turn. No lead is needed at this end of the coil. (Refer to Fig. 1 and Photo 1)

STEP 4. Spray the coil with three coats of acrylic and let it dry. (Refer to Photo 2)

STEP 5. The tuning capacitors are old units from junk AC/DC radios. The size and values of these are not critical as long as they are close to 320 - 365 pf per section. Remove the trimmer screws, mica, and trimmer plates. Clean up the connection lugs with a soldering iron. Scrape the rear corner of each capacitor case and solder a piece of hook-up wire, three inches long, to it. (Note: These capacitors can also be new units from one of the suppliers listed in the parts list.)

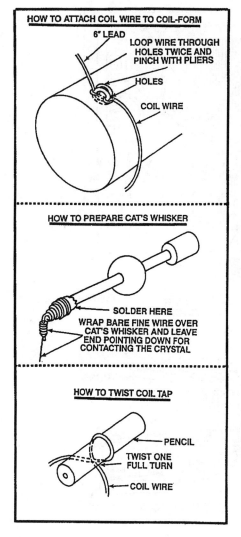

STEP 6. Place the tuning capacitors, coil, Fahnstock clips, and detector on the board as shown and outline their locations with a scribe or felt pen. (Refer to Figure 2)

STEP 7. Use super glue to attach two 3" x 1/4" wood strips, one inch apart, to the board for the coil mount, (I used balsawood). Glue the coil to the strips with super glue, with the taps pointed up and the lead to the left. (Refer to Photo 3)

STEP 8. Cut strips of double-sided foam mounting tape for holding the capacitors and press onto the board. Place the capacitors on the tape and press hard, being careful not to bend the capacitor plates. Install the knobs on both capacitors. (Refer to Photo 4)

Figure 1: Detailed drawings

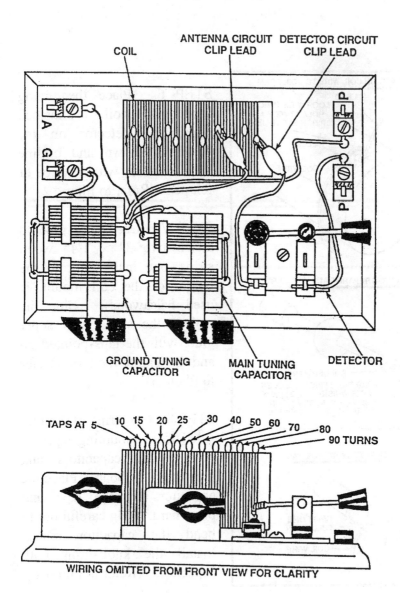

Figure 2: High performance crystal set

Photo 2: Finished coil before spraying with clear acrylic and trimming coil form

## Detector

STEP 9. (Refer to Figures 1 and 2)

You can use the mounted galena detector as shown, or you can mount two Fahnstock clips and install a 1N34 diode. The galena detector is a little more sensitive and selective, especially on short-wave, but is difficult to adjust. A 1N34 diode can be installed in the mounted detector clips also, as an alternative detector when not using the galena. This is recommended for testing the set because the diode will always work.

If you choose to use the galena detector, drill a small pilot hole to prevent the wood from splitting and mount with a wood screw. The cat's whisker should be soldered to the arm to make a good connection, and a short piece of bare, fine wire should be wrapped around the original cat's whisker and along its length. This will help with adjustment of the detector, because galena requires a light touch for maximum sensitivity.

STEP 10. Drill small pilot holes and mount the Fahnstock clips for the antenna, ground, and phones with wood screws (Refer to Figure 2).

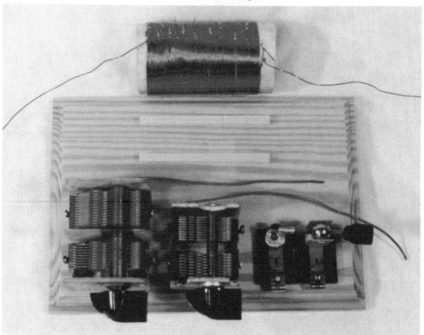

Photo 3: Location of coil mounting strips

## Wiring

STEP 11. Connect the coil antenna lead to the stator of the main tuning capacitor and then to the antenna clip. Be sure to scrape the enamel off of this wire where solder connections are made. Connect the stator sections of the main tuning capacitor together with a short piece of hook-up wire, then repeat the same on the ground tuning capacitor. (Refer to Figures 2 & 3, Photo 5)

The alligator clips used by the author were prefabricated test leads bought from Radio Shack with one clip removed. The builder can go with this option or fabricate his own. Make these leads as short as possible while still allowing slack to reach all the coil taps with both leads.

Connect the antenna circuit clip lead, rear phones clip, and rotor (case) of the main tuning capacitor to the rear stator lug of the ground tuning capacitor.

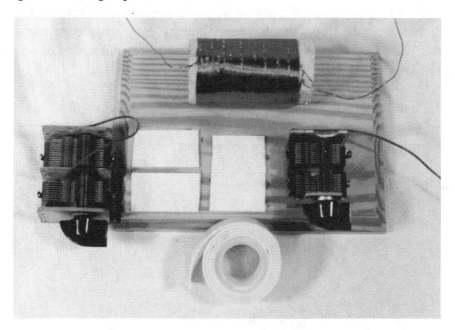

Photo 4: Installing double-sided foam mounting tape prior to securing tuning capacitors

Connect the rotor (case) of the ground tuning capacitor to the ground clip. Connect the detector circuit clip lead to the crystal side of the detector. Connect the front phones clip to the other side of the detector. (Note: Polarity of the detector usually doesn't make much difference. You can try either direction to see if you think it may work better one way or the other.)

Bend the coil taps alternately to the rear and to the front to facilitate connection with the clip leads. Then, scrape the enamel off of the taps where the clip leads grip them. Clip the antenna circuit clip lead to the 70th turn tap and the detector circuit lead to the 90th turn tap. This completes the wiring of the set.

## Antennas and Grounds

A good antenna and ground system is of utmost importance for satisfactory operation of a crystal set. Remember that your audio signal is only the signal that has been "caught" by your antenna wire after it has been tuned and detected. A short, low antenna will not give satisfactory results. (Refer to Photo 6)

The traditional rule-of-thumb on antennas is to "make them as long and as high as possible." Most of us have to compromise some on this rule, but follow it as much as you can. Most any kind of wire will work, or you may want to use one of the antenna kits referenced at the end of this article.

Photo 5: The completed high performance crystal set with 1N34A diode installed in detector clips for testing operation

The grounding system is also very important, especially on the lower frequencies. Cold water pipes used to be employed for this purpose, but now most houses are plumbed with PVC pipe, and this simply won't work as a ground because it is an insulator. The best ground to use is one of the ground stakes sold by Radio Shack or hardware stores.

CAUTION! Always disconnect your antenna when not in use and connect it to the ground. This will keep your antenna from building up a charge and will also provide a path for lightning in case you are unlucky enough to have your antenna "zapped" during a thunderstorm. Common sense tells us not to listen to crystal sets during stormy weather!

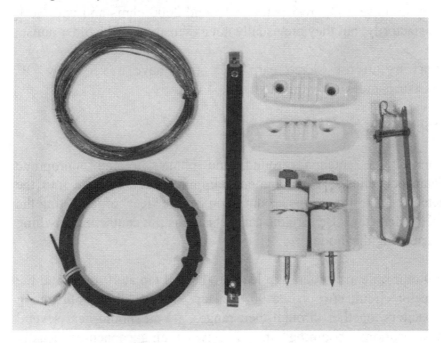

Photo 6: A typical fifty-foot outdoor antenna kit

## Headphones

The best headphones for crystal sets are the old high impedance magnetic phones that were used in the early days of radio and wireless. A minimum DC resistance of 2000 ohms is required and some of the old sets go to 4000 ohms and higher. The higher the DC resistance, the better, because they won't load down the crystal set as much as lower resistance units.

The next best choice is the Japanese piezoelectric crystal earplugs sold by Antique Electronic Supply. These use Rochelle salts crystals and have a DC resistance near infinity. They are not as loud as the magnetic phones, but make up for this because they plug directly into the ear. Two of these earplugs can be used, connected in parallel.

The last choice is the newly manufactured cheap magnetic head sets. They do have a DC resistance of around 2000 ohms and will work satisfactorily, but they are usually not as sensitive as the older units.

Don't try to use stereo earphones, they have a very low DC resistance and won't work at all.

## Operation

Connect the antenna, ground, and phones to the appropriate Fahnstock clips. I recommend clipping a 1N34 diode into the detector for testing purposes until you get the "feel" of adjusting the galena detector. Be sure the cat's whisker is not contacting anything when using the diode.

With the antenna circuit clip lead on the coil tap at 70 turns and the detector circuit clip on the 90 turn tap, slowly adjust both tuning capacitors together through their ranges. You should hear several A.M. stations "booming" in. The two tuning capacitors usually work well when tuned simultaneously to the same positions. You can experiment with different settings to your satisfaction.

The entire A.M. broadcast band can be received by moving the antenna circuit coil clip to various taps down to about the 30 turn tap. The detector circuit clip can be tried on any tap higher or lower than the antenna circuit tap for best volume and selectivity.

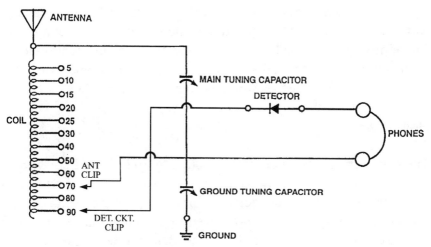

Figure 3: Schematic diagram

Short-wave stations in the 41 and 49 meter band and occasionally lower frequencies can be received at night on the taps at 5, 10, 15 and 20 turns. These signals will often alternately "fade" and "boom in" as the ionospheric charges build and fall. It is normal to hear more that one station at a time, but you can usually tune the weaker ones out.

The short-wave signals must "bounce" off the ionosphere, sometimes in several "hops" to the earth and back, to get to you from other parts of the planet. This ionospheric charging is dependent on the sun's activity, time of day, season of the year, and period within the eleven-year sunspot cycle. Some nights you may not receive anything, and other nights you will hear stations all over the globe.

A.M. broadcast DX is also possible with the same general rules as short-wave. The main difficulty here is to pull in the weak ones while being bombarded by strong local stations. K.E. Edwards' book, *Radios That Work for Free*, tells how to build an interference trap to help with this problem.

Best results with this little set will be obtained with practice, patience, and familiarity with tuning the capacitors, selecting taps, and adjusting the crystal. From our location we have heard eleven local stations on A.M. and short-wave stations in Europe, Australia, Africa, and the Far East, as well as several across the USA.

## How It Works

The main tuning capacitor, antenna circuit clip lead, and coil form a tuned circuit that will tune and pass a narrow band of frequencies from the antenna to the detector circuit. The detector circuit sensitivity and selectivity is optimized by selecting the best tap with the detector circuit clip lead. The detector rectifies the radio frequency signal and extracts the audio from it in order to drive the headphones. The ground tuning capacitor matches the antenna and ground circuit input to the tuned circuit made up by the main tuning capacitor and coil. (Refer to Figure 3)

## How to Adjust the Galena Detector

If you don't have much experience with open crystal detectors, use the 1N34 diode at first and tune in to a strong local station. Then disconnect the diode and lightly touch the cat's whisker to the galena crystal. You will find that the crystal has "hot" spots and "dead" spots. Find the loudest "hot" spot on your crystal and carefully adjust the cat's whisker pressure for optimum results.

You are now ready to try weaker stations. Once you have tuned to a weaker station, you will need to re-adjust the cat's whisker for the loudest output. After you practice this technique until you are comfortable with it, the diode can be removed. The galena usually is slightly more sensitive and selective on weaker signals. HAPPY DX-ing.

## Parts:

| | |
|---|---|
| Magnet wire, 1N34 diode, clips leads, antenna kits, ground rods, knobs | Radio Shack |
| Detectors, 1N34, diodes, clips leads, magnet wire, variable capacitors, knobs, antenna kits, headsets, piezo earplugs, fahnstock clips, crystal sets. | Xtal Set Society AES |

Double-sided mounting tape, routed boards, hardware store clear acrylic spray, screws, wire, ground rods

## References:

[1]Osterhoudt, Elmer G, *#2 crystal set circuit*, Modern Radio Laboratories.

[2]Edwards, K.E., *Radios That Work for Free*, Hope and Allen Publishing, Grants Pass, OR.

This project was originally seen in <u>Grid Leak</u> published by the Houston Vintage Radio Association. It was also reprinted in the <u>Electronics Handbook</u>, Volume XII. It is reprinted here by permission of Electronics Handbook.

# A Homemade Variable Capacitor and a Trap Tuned Set

by Eric Hudson

If you are not interested in buying or searching radio meets for a variable capacitor, or if your just a purist who wants to build everything from scratch, here is a great plan for a homemade one. You can make a variable capacitor from common lumber, aluminum foil, packaging tape, a short length of ½" OD plastic pipe or dowel and a few screws.

The capacitor described below could be used in many types of crystal radio projects. The circuit that attracted the writer's curiosity is one that relies on another one of those electronic mysteries, mutual induction. After you have made the capacitor, check out the second part of this article for a set to go with it.

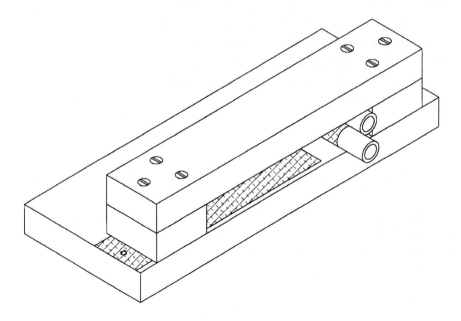

Figure 1: A homemade variable capacitor

The capacitor utilizes a mechanism known as a Rolamite bearing, which consists of two rollers and a flexible belt (aluminum foil-backed tape) operating between a pair of guides. The flexible belt, shown as a heavy line in Figure 2, has a pair of loops that cradle and suspend the rollers. Belt tension forces the rollers together and against the guides. Turning one roller causes both rollers to move in the guides.

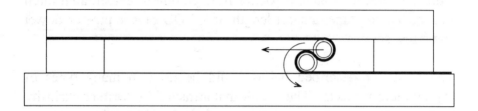

Figure 2: Rolamite bearing capacitor

A second strip of foil is glued to the bottom guide so that it is covered by the foil-backed tape as the rollers are moved to the left. Increasing the area of capacitor plates (foil) in close proximity increases the capacitance of the unit. The unit as shown should have an approximate range of 35 to 400 picofarads. Actual values depend upon how well the flexible belt is held against the stationary plate on the bottom guide.

## Construction

Cut a 10½" long piece of a 1 x 4 for the bottom guide. Note: the actual finished size of a 1 x 4 is ¾" x 3½", in case you are ripping up a larger piece for the bottom guide. The 1 x 4 should provide enough room to serve as a base for the rest of the radio circuit behind the capacitor. The capacitor dimensions can be changed to suit your taste and requirements.

The next phase is to make a bridge-like structure out of 1 x 2's (actually, ¾" x 1½"). As shown in Figures 3 and 4, the top piece is 9½" long and the two short spacers are 1½" long. Twelve, No. 8,

1¼" long brass screws fasten the wooden pieces together. Pre-drill the screw holes with the pieces clamped in position and then screw the wooden pieces together without the foil plates initially. Remove any burrs that are raised during drilling so that the pieces will fit tightly together. Offset the location of the screw holes as shown in Figure 3 to prevent the lower screws from coming into contact with the upper screws.

Improvise if you must, but bear in mind that the spacer on the left will separate the two foil plates of the capacitor, so it is important that the screws used for assembly do not penetrate all the way through this spacer. Otherwise, an electrical short between the plates will be created. There is no such problem on the right hand side.

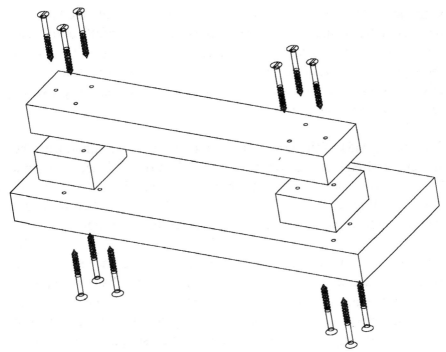

Figure 3: Wooden guide

Make the stationary plate of the capacitor from a strip of aluminum foil glued to the bottom guide. It is probably easiest to glue an oversized piece onto the guide and trim it to size, peeling away the excess before the glue sets completely. A thin liquid glue is needed so that the foil can be smoothed out flat onto the base. Elmer's Liquid School Glue Gel, works fine. A rubber cement should also work. Work out the excess and wipe clean. Flatness and smoothness are required for good operation. Use a straight blade and a very sharp knife or razor blade to trim the foil to size (see Figures 1 and 4). A dull edge will tend to tear the foil.

The other capacitor plate and dielectric is constructed of aluminum foil and 2" wide plastic packaging tape. Lay a strip of the tape, about a foot and a half long, sticky side up on a table or counter top. A good way to do this is to fold an inch or so of the end of the tape over, and put this sticky side down a foot and a half from the edge of a counter top, and then let the roll hang down a bit over the edge with the sticky side out. The weight of the roll will hold the tape flat on the counter while an oversized piece of foil is carefully applied to the sticky side of the tape laying on the counter. Start at the end of the tape and use your fingers or a cylindrical object to smooth out any wrinkles in the foil as it is applied to the tape and to press the foil down firmly onto the adhesive.

Cut off the ends of the tape that are not covered by foil and trim the foil covered tape to the width of a 1 x 2 board ( 1½" actual) with a knife or razor blade and a cutting board. Note: The stationary foil plate (see Figure 4) is 1¼" narrower than the flexible belt to insure that the dielectric overlaps the edges, preventing shorting.

Lay the foil-covered tape, tape side down, along the edge of the bottom guide, so it overlaps the right side of the base perhaps an 1/8" and extends over the other foil plate and beyond the left side of the base. Screw the right side spacer in place over the foil-backed tape while taking care to keep the tape aligned straight with the front edge of the bottom guide.

The left side spacer can now be screwed onto the bottom guide. The foil-backed tape must be lifted temporarily out of the way on the left side as the spacer will be under the tape.

Lay the foil-backed tape over the left side spacer. Attach the top guide piece firmly to <u>only</u> the right side spacer, with screws.

Cut two ½" diameter rollers from plastic pipe, wooden dowel stock or similar type of non-magnetic material. The top roller is 1⅝ to 1¾" long. The lower roller is 2⅛ to 2¼" long. The more perfectly round these rollers are, the better they will roll in the final product. Take the time to de-burr the edges of the rollers after cutting them, with a file or sand paper.

The foil-backed tape must be finessed into a reverse 'S' shape (heavy line Figure 2) in between the top and bottom guides in order to insert the rollers. A couple of pencils should help you to form the loops. Make the loops oversized so that the rollers can be inserted. Later, tension will tighten the loops. The long lower roller is installed into the left loop and the short upper roller is put into the loop to the right. The short roller should be centered in the tape. The extra length of the long roller should extend ½" over the edge of the guide, to act as a tuning knob, and the opposite end should be flush with the short roller.

When the rollers are in place, apply a little tension to the end of the foil backed tape sticking out from under the left hand side of the top guide. This will pull the rollers together. Turn the long roller between you fingers while maintaining tension on the tape with the other hand. It should roll smoothly back and forth in between the base and top guide. Correct any misalignment of the roller paths by adjusting the amount of tension on each edge of the tape and by slight changes in the roller alignment within the tape. Also work to have the tape lay flat over the other capacitor plate as the rollers are moved to the left. Turn the rollers for the entire length of the guides between the spacers during your alignment trials. This alignment process may take a few minutes of trial and error.

When you are satisfied that the rollers and tape are in the best possible alignment, install the screws that hold the left side of the top guide to the support while maintaining the correct position and tension on the tape. A clamp or helper bearing down on the top guide is a good idea at this point. If you have not pre-drilled the screw holes and previously assembled the guide to the support you will have difficulty doing this operation.

Test the action of the rollers. Look at the joints and make sure that no light passes between them when you hold them up. The excess tape can be trimmed at the support on the left and at the edge of the base on the right.

Two small screws, No. 4's, ½" long, are centered in the foil extending out on each side of the base. These screws are the connections for the capacitor.

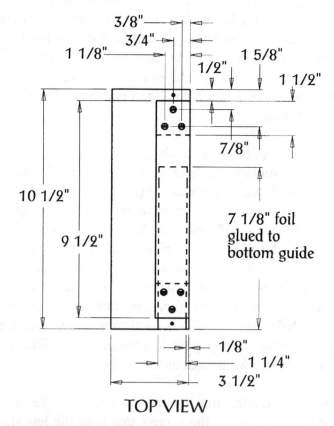

TOP VIEW

Figure 4: Guide measurements

## A Trap Tuned Radio Set to Use with the Capacitor

The circuit is a modified version of design 'E' that appears in Midco's catalog (see vendor section at the back of this book) and in Figure 3-4C of P. A. Kinzie's excellent book, *Crystal Radio: History, Fundamentals, and Design*. The modification consists of changing the coil dimensions so that plastic coated bell wire can be used instead of the enameled wire specified in the original Midco design and eliminating a capacitor from both versions. The plastic-coated wire was easier to obtain than enameled wire.

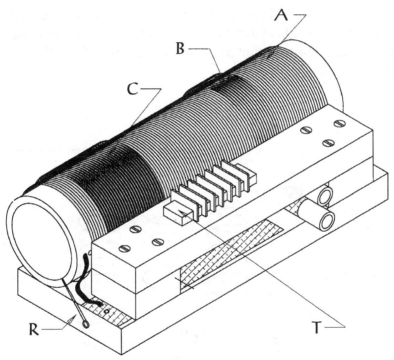

Figure 5: Pictorial view, *A*-tuning coil, 126 turns of 18 gauge plastic coated wire; *B*-10 turns 18 gauge wire over tuning coil; *C*-25 turns 18 gauge wire over tuning coil; *T*- terminal block; *R*-rubber band.

The coil form is a 10½" long piece of 2" ID PVC heavy wall pipe having an OD of 2 3/8". Two 1/8" holes were drilled ½" from each end of the pipe and a 9½" long, 126 turn tuning coil was wound between them out of 18 gauge plastic coated wire. The .075" diameter of the plastic insulation allows about 15 turns per inch. A 25 turn detector coil was wound, from the same wire, directly on top of the initial coil near one end. A 10 turn antenna coupling coil was wound near the other. It may be wise to put a layer of cardboard from a cereal box in between the antenna coil and the first coil to reduce the amount of coupling for better selectivity.

A terminal block with six connections was mounted on top of the capacitor, as shown, to facilitate circuit wiring. Although I used screw terminals, Fahnstock spring clips would also work nicely (refer to Figure 6 for connections). The coil was held onto the base with a rubber band hooked over two small screws on each side. This allowed quick adjustments to coils. Note that there is room on top of the capacitor to mount a catwhisker detector, if you desire, instead of a 1N34 diode.

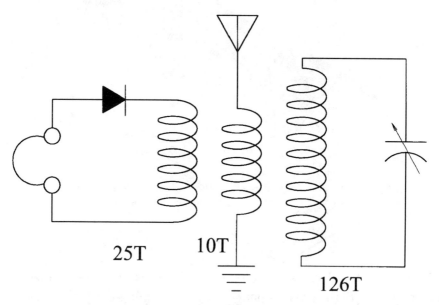

Figure 6: Schematic diagram, detector coil at left, antenna coupling coil center, tuning coil at right.

The use of plastic coated wire instead of enameled wire uses more feet of wire but, according to published formulas, should give a higher 'Q'. Again, the availability governed the author's choice.

The author has connected two such radios to a long wire antenna and found that stations over 300 miles away could be heard. The circuit appears very willing to resonate in response to frequencies at harmonic intervals and the same station can sometimes be heard at two tuning locations.

Two thousand ohm headphones work well with the circuit. The element from a telephone handset was usable, but it did not perform as well as headphones; telephone headsets are only a few hundred ohms.

## About the Author

A mechanical engineer, (BSME, Washington University), Eric Hudson designs internal combustion engines.

Nevertheless, a crystal radio was an excellent project with which his seven year old son, Bill, could be introduced to electronics and learn about the existence of two important facets: electromagnetic waves and solid state junctions.

After all, what better way could there be to show the existence of radio waves than to capture some of these waves and put them to use without the help of outside power? And, in this age of microchips, where the densities of circuits are hard for many of us to comprehend, doesn't the crystal detector illustrate, better than anything else, the physical embodiment of a solid state junction?

There was also a certain boyhood excitement associated with the 40 year old memory of a Cub Scout crystal set, with its antenna wire wound around the perimeter of the bunk bed posts. The author wanted to share the excitement and history of crystal sets with his son.

With the help of knowledge gained from the Xtal Set Society books and from Dr. B. A. Turke of MIDCO, Eric and Bill were able to build sets that exceeded the performance of the old Cub Scout model.

Along the way to constructing the set there was the frustrating experience of receiving a blank look from the salesman, in an electronics store, when inquiry was made about variable capacitors. That experience provided the inspiration for this article.

# Build a Matchbox Crystal Radio
by Jim Clark

In my first year of high school, the final project in my electronics class was to build a crystal radio. It was a fairly massive thing, built on a homemade aluminum chassis. The 365 pf tuning capacitor was the air-gap type typically found in the vacuum tube radios of that era. The coil was wound on a toilet paper roll using #22 enameled wire. As I recall, the primary coil, which went to the antenna and ground, was fifteen turns. The secondary, which was wound beside the primary and hooked in parallel with the tuning capacitor, was sixty to ninety turns. This ratio stepped up the signal received by the primary. The number of turns in the secondary provided the correct inductance, required by the parallel LC network, to tune in the broadcast band. The detector was the venerable 1N34 germanium diode, and the output fed to 2000 ohm headphones via a pair of fahnestock clips. The radio worked, and was capable of picking up two of the local AM stations. It was not a great performer, but at least it did work. I derived much satisfaction from having the ability to pluck radio signals from the ether at no cost, with a device that I had built.

The only problem with this creation, as mentioned before, was it's size, which did not lend itself to portability. I decided there must be a way to make a miniature version and began scrounging parts for the project (see Table 1: Parts List and Sources). My first challenge was to find a suitable container. After searching around my parent's house, I came up with the perfect thing—a regular size box of Fire Chief Matches. My goal was to have the entire unit self-contained, including the earphone, so my next challenge was to locate parts that would fit into a box that was 2" long, 1 2/3" wide and 3/4" deep. I knew that I would have to use a high impedance ceramic crystal-type earphone, which would fill up almost half the box. The coil and tuning capacitor were both scavenged from a dead 6-transistor radio. The coil was the type that had a ferrite tuning slug. It was adjusted by turning the tuning shaft which was threaded through a metal mounting bracket at one end of the coil. I cut the bracket off the end of the coil form; this made the coil short enough to fit into my box, and also enabled the slug to move back and forth freely by simply tilting the box. The 365 pf tuning capacitor was the old aluminum plate and mylar insulator type without an enclosure, and it measured about 1" square by 2/3" thick. Again, the detector was the old reliable 1N34. Once the parts were assembled using the schematic shown in Figure 1, I rigged up a short piece of stranded wire with an alligator clip at each end to connect the radio to an antenna. I found that I could connect the antenna to either lug on the coil, or to either lug or even the tuning shaft on the capacitor with equal results. I also found that clipping the lead to many metal parts (lamp bases, etc.) or to long cords such as a telephone cord gave surprisingly good results for the antenna. No ground connection was necessary, although using one theoretically should improve performance. As with it's larger brother, my miniature radio was able to pick up a couple of the local stations. Tuning was accomplished by turning the tuning shaft of the capacitor and tilting the box to slide the ferrite slug to different positions in the coil form.

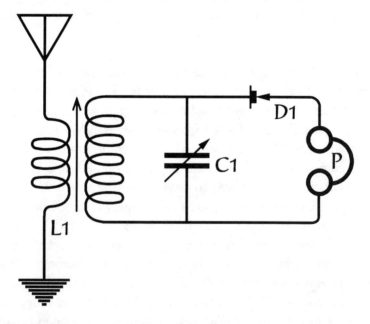

Figure 1: Matchbox crystal radio

Selectivity and sensitivity were not the best in the world by any means, but I had what I believe at the time was the world's smallest self-contained crystal set, and it worked! Photo 1 shows the assembled parts ready to be housed in the matchbox, and Photo 2 shows them in place. A bit of rearranging of the positions of the parts was required to get everything to fit. Unfortunately, I was unable to find room for the clear plastic earpiece on the earphone, so I had to remove it.

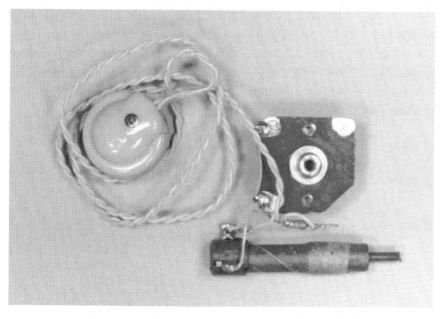

Photo 1: Matchbox radio parts

Modern-day equivalents for the parts I used are available, so you can build your own matchbox radio. A list of suppliers and part numbers appears at the end of this chapter. As seen in Photo 3, there are five different capacitors that should work quite nicely. The two enclosed types each have two separate sections which will need to be hooked in parallel. One will result in a 10 to 200 pf range, while the other will result in a 10 to 532 pf range. The 365 pf unit like I used is periodically available, but it may take some searching to locate. Two trimmer capacitors are shown—the one with the screw adjustment is 40 to 500 pf, and the one with the shaft is 20 to 300 pf. Numerous other values are available. If you elect to use one with a shaft, you will need to cut off most of the shaft in order to fit it into the box. An advantage to using one of the enclosed capacitors, or one of the trimmer capacitors, is that you may save enough space in the box for the earphone earpiece. When buying the earphone, make sure that it is the ceramic crystal type and not the dynamic type. The crystal variety will usually be tan in color and will frequently be marked "Crystal Receiver" on the earphone itself. The dynamic types are usually white in color and are not as large as the crystal type. The coil that is currently available also has a ferrite tuning slug, but it is the type that is threaded inside the coil form and is adjusted by using a 2.5mm or 0.100" nylon hex-type alignment tool. A schematic comes with the coil to show how to connect it to the circuit. This coil is shorter than my original and will fit into the matchbox without removing the metal mounting bracket.

Photo 2: Matchbox crystal radio in box

Feel free to experiment with my basic design and see how you can improve or customize it for your particular taste. For example, if you do not care to keep the earphone in the box, then you can install a miniature phone jack in one end of the matchbox drawer to plug the earphone into. You could also use the mounting bracket for the coil in the opposite end of the drawer, so that the tuning slug could be adjusted from the outside. If you choose to go with either (or both) of these options, I would recommend that you reinforce the inside surface of the drawer ends with thin aluminum or brass inserts, cut to size and with the appropriately sized drill holes. Otherwise, the drawer ends might eventually tear from the stress. You could also make a small hole in the top of the box that aligns with the tuning capacitor, so that it can be adjusted with the box closed. You might want to solder fine-gauge antenna and ground wires to the coil, and just keep them wrapped around the box when you're not using the radio. Use your imagination, and I'm sure that you will be as proud of your *Matchbox Crystal Radio* as I am of mine!

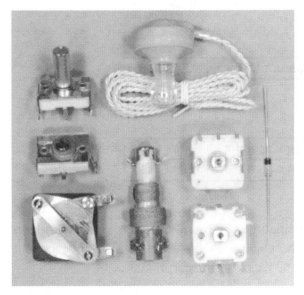

Photo 3: Top and center left, two trimmer capacitors; top center, crystal earphone; bottom left, variable capacitor; bottom center, coil; bottom right, two enclosed variable capacitors; far right, diode.

## Table 1: Parts List and Sources

Antique Electronic Supply
(see vendor section on page 155 for their address)

| L1 | Antenna Coil | # P-C70-A |
|----|--------------|-----------|
| L1 | Alignment Tool | # S-T9302 |
| C1 | 40-500 Trimmer Capacitor | # C-VT500 |

Circuit Specialists, Inc.
(see vendor section on page 155 for their address)

| C1 | 10-200 pf Tuning Capacitor | # 24TR222 |
|----|----------------------------|-----------|
| C1 | 10-532 pf Tuning Capacitor | # 24TR218 |
| C1 | Trimmer Capacitors are available | |
| D1 | 1N34 Germanium Diode | # 1N34 |

Radio Shack

| D1 | 1N34A Germanium Diode | #276-1123 |
|----|----------------------|-----------|

Xtal Set Society

| C1 | 0-365 pf Tuning Capacitor | 365 |
|----|---------------------------|-----|
| P | Crystal Earphone | Ear |

Crystal earphones can sometimes be found at Radio Shack, although they are not listed in the catalog. This store is also an excellent source for miniature phone jacks for the earphones.

## About The Author

Jim Clark first developed an interest in electronics when he entered high school, where he took electronics classes all four years. It was during his freshman year that he built his first crystal set. His interest in the subject stayed with him in later years, and he spent much of his spare time tinkering and building projects published in Electronics Illustrated and Popular Electronics. After attending college at the University of Tennessee, he decided to pursue a career in the electronics field and obtained his degree from the Tennessee Institute of Electronics. He is currently Facility Director of the Electron Microprobe Laboratory at Arizona State University, where he has worked for the past eighteen years. Jim, his wife Pat and son Patrick share a common interest in antiques, with one of Jim's main interests being the collection and restoration of antique radios. As well as being a member of the Xtal Set Society, he also belongs to the Antique Wireless Association and the Arizona Antique Radio Club.

# A Krystal Kludge
by William Simes

As long as I can remember, building things has been a favorite pastime. As a kid, building things from junk was a necessity. As a retiree it's a fascination which led to the assembly described here. Hopefully, some of the findings will be of interest to the xtal set experimenters.

The circuit is shown in Figure 1. It consists of a loop antenna, a tuning capacitor, a detector, and a sound transducer. The components are interconnected with clip leads (radio shack part number 278-1156.)

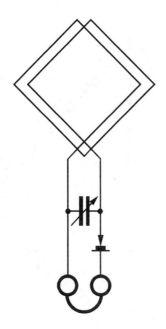

Figure 1: Schematic of the krystal kludge set

## The Loop

Our house is located three miles from WDAF and six miles from KMBZ. Both are 5 kilowatt stations. I was pleasantly surprised to receive signals from each station using only a tuned loop antenna with a crystal detector. This was particularly surprising because the loop was in the basement! Of the loop configurations I've tried, the one shown in Figures 2 and 3 is my favorite. The taps at each turn can be used for changing inductance and for load matching. The loop can be readily removed from its base for storage. In my case, when the loop is not in use, it hangs from two hooks fastened to a basement ceiling joist. The base stores easily between joists. The maximum inductance of the loop is about 210 μH. Lower values of inductance are accessible using the taps. As measured from the outside (no. 1 tap) to the Nth tap, the inductance is approximately $2.25 \times N^2$ μH.

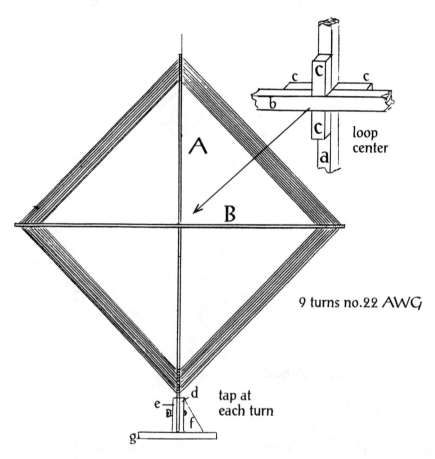

Figure 2: Loop antenna

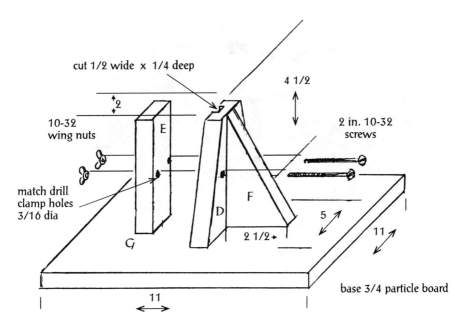

cut 1/2 wide x 1/4 deep

4 1/2

10-32
wing nuts

2 in. 10-32
screws

match drill
clamp holes
3/16 dia

base 3/4 particle board

Figure 3: Loop base detail (dimensions in inches)

## The Capacitor

To my knowledge, the capacitor used here is unique. In an attempt to make the capacitance of a Leyden jar variable for the tuning loop, I covered the outside of a half-gallon fruit jar with Reynolds wrap, put a copper strip inside, and connected the strip and foil to the loop terminals. This was paralleled with headphones in series with a diode. I listened as saturated salt water was poured in the jar. Sure enough, as the level rose, stations came and went. When I replaced the fruit jar with a two-liter coke bottle, performance improved. The bottle capacity changed about 100pf for each inch change in electrolyte level. The inconvenience of a one-way variable capacitor operated by pouring electrolyte from one container to another left too much to be desired. What was needed was a sealed bottle that allowed capacity to be increased or decreased without electrical connections to the electrolyte. The need was met with the holder and bottle configuration shown in Figure 4.

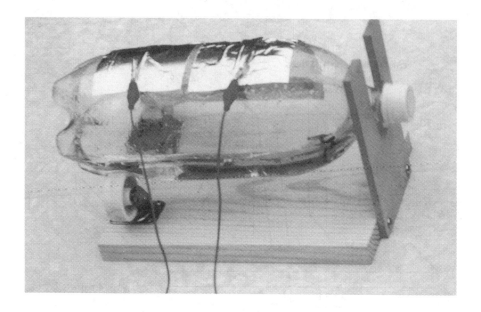

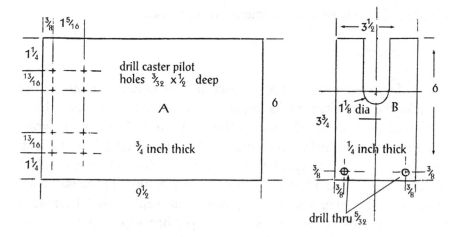

Figure 4: Capacitor assembly and base detail (dimensions in inches)

The base assembly is straightforward. Its function is to hold the bottle so as to allow its axial rotation while positioned horizontally. Preparing the bottle to make it a capacitor may take some patience. Here are some suggestions: First, fill the bottle with hot (55°C) water; usually hot tap water will work. In a short time heat from the water softens the adhesive that holds on the label and bottom cup, (if there is a bottom cup). Next, remove the label (and the cup) and, with the hot water still in the bottle, clean off any residual adhesive using Gumout (or other suitable solvent) and a paper towel. Two-inch Tuck Aluminum tape (Tesa Tuck, Inc. New Rochelle, NY) available at most building supply stores can be used to form the external electrodes. One side of the tape has an adhesive coating with a paper backing. Once a bottle is cleaned and the aluminum tape is available, follow this procedure.

1) Stretch a rubber band about the bottle and align it to locate the bottle's center.

2) Cut 4 strips of aluminum tape 7 inches long. Adjusting the tape position after its adhesive makes contact is difficult, so before removing the backing, fold over about ½ inch of tape along its long edge. Make the fold with the backing on the outside of the fold.

3) Carefully remove the backing from all but the ½ inch fold-over.

4) Pull the tape taut, align its unfolded edge with the lower edge of the centered rubber band apply the tape to the bottle.

5) Once in place, remove the backing from the folded section.

6) Remove the entire backing from another 7-inch length of tape. Pull the tape taut and align its edge with the exposed adhesive on the folded edge of the tape already in place first. Make the contact between the 2 strips of tape and between the second tape and the bottle, and smooth out any wrinkles.

7) Repeat this procedure to apply the electrode to the upper half of the bottle.

8) Fold up the corners of the half-inch ridges on both electrodes. This exposes some electrode surface without adhesive, allowing clip lead contact to both halves of each electrode.

An electrolyte is needed to complete the electrolytic variable capacitor. Saturated salt water works. It is cheap and it is benign. I found the unloaded signal level of a local station tuned with the salt water capacitor to be about 27 mV. The same station tuned with an air dielectric capacitor showed an unloaded level of about 150 mV. By adding 21 ohms in series with the air capacitor, the signal level mated that of the salt-water capacitor. There are, of course, stronger electrolytes. Here is one that worked better:

One quart of water was added to an empty bottle with external electrodes attached as described above. To this, 100ml of Muriatic acid (31.4% HC1) was added. It behaved as a capacitor, but the capacity didn't change much when the bottle was rotated. The conductive wet coating inside the bottle left the electrolyte area inside the bottle poorly defined. This was corrected by adding a pint of so of kerosene which provided an insulating layer that floated on the electrolyte. The capacity then changed as expected when the bottle was rotated. The signal degradation using this capacitor was equivalent to adding 6 ohms to the air capacitor. Its tuning range was about 100 to 480 pf. Oil floating over the electrolyte further reduces the trapped air volume and the bottle distortions associated with temperature induced volumetric changes. On the other hand, it also tends to increase weight. Replacing the base cup on the bottle could prevent this distortion.

## The Detector

The 1N34A diode is handy, cheap and works every time. However, for the purist bent on a junk assembly, try this. It's tacky, but it worked for me. Find a mouse trap, preferably one that hasn't served its intended purpose. Remove the bait holder and trip wire. That leaves only the spring-load rectangular business piece. This wire piece is then used to hold the galena firmly against the wood base.

In so doing, it makes good electrical contact with the galena and provides a contact on which to fasten a clip lead. A small jelly glass with a suitable length of fine wire fastened to its top with a rubber band makes a functional cat whisker. After a few turns of the fine wire on the clip lead clip, the edge of the glass makes a good anchor for the clip lead (Figure 5). The fine wire can be removed from a section of stranded hook-up wire. Now position the jelly glass assembly so the cat whisker makes the right contact with the galena and you have a detector. Again, it's tacky, it's functional, and it's sometimes a good conversation piece for an otherwise disinterested visitor.

Figure 5: Krystal kludge set

## The Transducer (Headphone)

High-impedance store-bought headphones work well. For the purist again, the piezoelectric transducer made from a cat food can is recommended. Such a device is detailed in Vol 6, No. 3 of the Xtal Set Society Newsletter.

As a rural kid, I could only get Dr. Brinkly on my crystal set. Now I'm geographically blessed with a location where a crystal set can receive many stations (not always better programs). A more geographically challenged crystal set experimentalist may need younger ears to share my results.

# A Triple Tuned Crystal Set
by Greg Constant

I have built several crystal sets over the years, and I enjoyed the challenge of optimizing each one for best reception. I have always lived in urban areas and have found that it is sometimes difficult to obtain good performance from single or double tuned sets due to nearby stations. In addition, I have used antennas of many different lengths because of limited available space. My latest set was intended to address both of these issues. This set is a standard AM broadcast band crystal receiver which was designed to provide increased selectivity over single or double tuned sets and to be a little more tolerant of different types of antennas. This set is somewhat more complex than the ones I've built in the past, in that it has several more controls to operate, but since every crystal set requires a lot of experimentation to optimize it for best performance in any given situation, I have found the added front panel controls to be worth the extra effort.

As you can see from the schematic in Fig. 1, this set is composed of three separate tuned circuits. The broadcast band signal is picked up by the antenna and fed to the first circuit, the antenna tuner. This circuit peaks the antenna response for the desired listening frequency. Besides the antenna tuning control, two switches are provided which allow the antenna coil inductance and tuning type (series/parallel etc.) to be easily varied to best match the antenna impedance to the set. This allows the set to accommodate antennas of varying length. The tuned RF signal is inductively coupled from the antenna circuit to the second tuned circuit, the detector tank. This L-C circuit again peaks the received RF signal which is then coupled to the detector to be converted into audio. A switch is provided to vary the detector coupling in order to maximize the received audio volume. The third tuned circuit, which is also inductively coupled to the antenna, is the interference trap. This resonant tank enhances the selectivity of the set by providing the ability to null out an interfering station so that an adjacent signal can be received clearly.

Crystal Set Projects

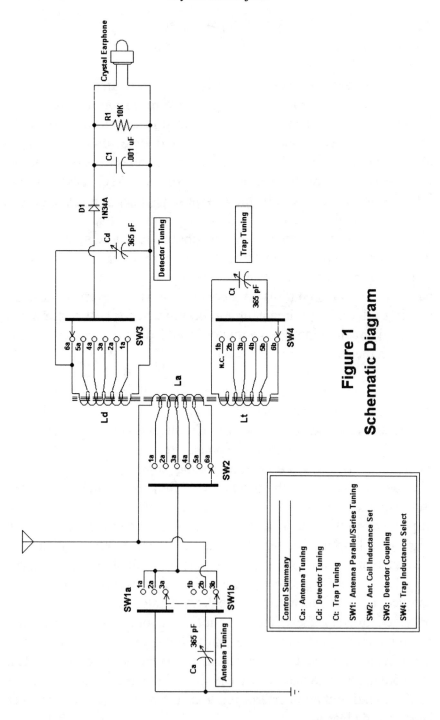

Figure 1
Schematic Diagram

112

This feature comes in very handy if the set is operated near one or more strong local stations. All three coils in this set are wound on a ferrite rod which produces a higher Q tuned circuit than that of air core coils, resulting in greater selectivity and sensitivity.

## Set Construction

I constructed my set on a homemade "L" chassis made of a piece of masonite for the front panel and a piece of ¾ inch pine board for the base. The basic front panel layout, chassis construction, and component placement are illustrated in Figures 2 and 3. Begin construction by cutting out a 5½" x 11" piece of pine board for the chassis base. Sand all edges smooth with fine grit sand paper after cutting the board to size. Next, cut out a 5¾" x 11" piece of masonite for the front panel. Determine where the three variable capacitors, the four rotary switches, the antenna and ground terminals, and the earphone terminals will be located on the front panel, and then drill appropriately sized holes for each of them in the piece of masonite. Sand all edges smooth with fine grit sand paper when the cutting and drilling are finished. You may wish to paint the front panel if you want your set to have a cleaner look. To give the set an antique appearance, spray paint the masonite front panel with flat black paint. When this dries apply a coat of clear matte spray finish and let dry. Then lightly and evenly buff the clear matte with very fine steel wool. Next spray on one more coat of clear matte and, after allowing it to dry, again buff it very lightly with very fine steel wool. This will produce a finish that closely resembles Bakelite, a material commonly used for front panels in early radio receivers. After the front panel is drilled, sanded and painted to your liking, fasten it to the base with three small wood screws.

Now mount all of the variable capacitors, rotary switches and binding posts to the front panel. Use Fig. 2 and Fig. 3 as guides for component placement. Mount the three variable capacitors onto the front panel by using small self-tapping sheet metal screws through the mounting holes on the front of the capacitor frames. Make sure that the variable capacitor mounting screws are not long enough to interfere with the stator or rotor plates when the shaft is rotated. If no screw holes are provided on your particular capacitors, use a strong adhesive to glue them to the front panel. Now mount the four rotary switches on the front panel after cutting the length of their shafts down with a hack saw. Trim the shafts so that about ½ inch will protrude from the front panel after the switches are mounted. Next mount the antenna, ground and earphone binding posts onto the front panel as shown in the diagrams. Note that the crystal earphone given in the parts list comes with a 3.5 mm plug. If you have a 3.5 mm earphone jack available you can use it in place of the earphone binding posts. Otherwise just cut off the plug, tin the wires with solder, and connect the earphones to the binding posts.

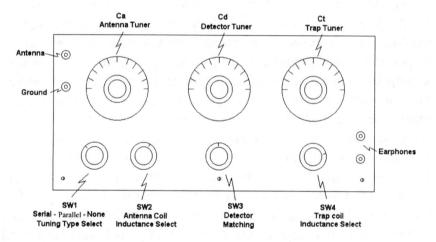

Figure 2: Front panel layout

The front panel is now complete, so next assemble the detector circuit which consists of diode D1, capacitor C1 and resistor R1. Use small wood screws to mount the two terminal strips onto the chassis base next to each other and about 1½ inches apart, as shown in Fig 3. Solder the diode, capacitor and resistor to the terminal strips as shown in the diagram. Note that the polarity of the crystal diode is not critical. The circuit will function the same no matter which way it is connected.

The last assembly to construct will be the three coils which are wound on a single 5 inch long, 11/32 inch diameter ferrite rod. Note that the ferrite rod is very fragile and will break easily, so be careful while winding the coils. Using 30 gauge wire, start at about 1/4 inch from one end of the ferrite rod and begin winding the antenna coil La. This coil will have a total of 70 turns and 5 taps. First wind 10 turns onto the rod and then make a tap by making a small loop in the wire and twisting it tight. Make the tap stick out about 1/2 inch from the coil. Continue winding 40 more turns of wire, making a tap after every 10 turns. Finish this coil up by winding 20 more turns with no taps. Make sure all of turns are wound tightly and closely spaced. Fasten the wires at each end of the coil to the ferrite rod using a strong adhesive tape. Next wind the detector coil Ld in the middle of the rod. Ld consists of 70 turns total and has 5 taps, the same as the antenna coil, so wind this coil in exactly the same manner as the first coil. Leave about 1/4 inch of space between the two coils. Last wind the interference trap coil Lt on the other end of the ferrite rod. Lt is wound with a total of 70 turns in the same manner as the first two, except that it only needs to have four taps instead of five. So wind 10 turns, make and a tap, then wind 30 more turns with a tap after every 10 turns. After the fourth tap, wind 30 more turns with no taps. Again leave about 1/4 inch of space between this coil and the previous one. After all three coils are wound and fastened to the ferrite rod, carefully strip the insulation off of all the taps and end point wires and tin them with a little solder. Mount the coil assembly to the wood chassis base using silicone cement at each end of the ferrite rod. Orient the coils so that all of the taps protrude upwards for easy access and so that the antenna coil La is toward the side of the set containing the antenna terminal, as shown in Fig. 3.

Now that all components are mounted onto the chassis, make all of the required connections using any type of hook-up wire that you have available. If you would like the internal part of the set to have an antique look, use the black lacquered cloth covered wire from the supplier given in the parts list. This type of wire closely resembles hook up wire used in early receivers. Using the hookup wire, solder all of the connections called for in the schematic diagram. A pictorial diagram of all components and connections is also given in Fig. 4 to aid in this final step. This diagram is basically a view from the rear of the set with all of the parts arranged for clarity.

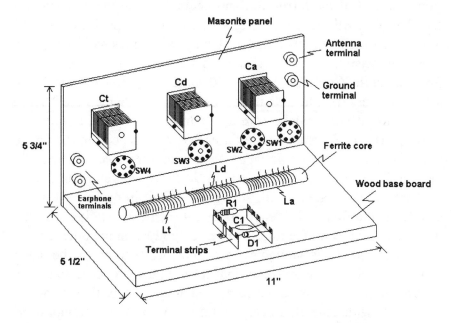

Figure 3: Rear view of set with all components mounted

Once all of the components are connected up properly, install knobs on all of the front panel controls. All of the controls on this set have 1/4" shafts, so choose knobs which are sized for these shafts. Other than the shaft sizes the knob types are not important, they are just a matter of personal taste. If you have some antique knobs in your junk box, or ones you can salvage from an old radio, this project would be an excellent use for them. Otherwise there are many types of 1/4" knobs available from the sources given in the parts list, so choose the ones that suit your preferences.

## Set Operation

Connect your earphone, antenna and ground to the appropriate terminals on the front panel. Your antenna should be a single wire, as long and as high above the ground as possible. Your ground connection can be a metal cold water pipe, or if one is not available, a metal rod driven 4 - 8 feet into the soil. Familiarize yourself with the front panel controls shown in Fig. 2. The leftmost control, variable capacitor Ca, is the antenna tuning control. Rotating this control will peak the antenna circuit for the desired station. Below this is switch SW1, which controls whether Ca is in parallel or in series with the antenna coil La, or whether capacitor Ca is not connected to the antenna coil at all. Since every antenna has a different characteristic impedance, which varies with length, you will need to select the tuning type which best suits your particular antenna. Switch SW1 provides this flexibility. With a good long antenna (150 ft or greater) series tuning will produce the best performance. A shorter antenna will probably perform best with a parallel tuned configuration, and a very short antenna may perform best with no antenna tuning at all. Rotating SW1 all the way to the left will select no tuning for the antenna circuit. One position to the right of this will select parallel tuning and the third position will select series tuning. Experiment with all three settings to find out which one gives the best performance for your antenna. Switch SW2, also located below the antenna tuning control, is used to adjust the inductance of the antenna coil La. Once again, depending on the length of your antenna, different inductance values may be needed to resonate the antenna to the frequency you want to listen to, so SW2 provides this capability. Rotating SW2 to the left lowers the inductance of La and rotating it to the right raises the inductance. Select the position that maximizes the received volume of the station you are trying to tune in.

The detector tuning control, capacitor Cd, is located in the middle of the front panel. It is used to tune the detector coil, Ld, to the desired listening frequency. Switch SW3, located below Cd, is used to maximize the audio provided by the detector by adjusting the coupling between the detector tank and the detector circuit. After the antenna circuit is peaked to the desired station, use Cd to maximize the signal for the station you are listening to. Then rotate SW3 to find the point which results in maximum audio in the earphones.

Note that the antenna and detector tuning controls may interact slightly so in general you will need to rotate both at the same time in order to search for stations. Experiment with these controls and you will soon get used to tuning this set.

The remaining two controls on the right side of the front panel form the interference trap. If you find that a strong local station is drowning out part of the band or if two equal strength stations are coming in at the same time, you can use the trap tuning control Ct and switch SW4 to cancel out the interfering signal. Always start your listening session with SW4 rotated all the way to the left. This position disconnects Lt and Ct, thereby disabling the interference trap circuit. If you find that a signal is interfering with the station that you are trying to listen to, rotate SW4 to the right and select the position that allows you to best null out the offending signal by rotating the trap tuning control. Once the signal is canceled out you can leave SW4 and Ct in their current positions and tune through the band using the antenna and detector tuning controls.

## A Word About Parts

Sources for all electrical parts for this set are given in the parts list at the end of this project; however, it isn't necessary to use the exact parts shown. Half the fun of building a crystal set can be locating good used parts, or possibly even authentic antique parts. The air-dielectric 365 pF variable capacitors as well as the ferrite core can be obtained from older tube type receivers. These parts can also be obtained from newer transistorized AM radios, although the variable capacitors may be the smaller plastic dielectric types. Most of the other parts needed for this set, except possibly the rotary switches, could also be obtained from a junked radio. So scrounge around a little at junk shops, antique shops or garage sales to see what you can find. It will be worth the trouble and it will be fun at the same time.

# A Triple Tuned Crystal Set

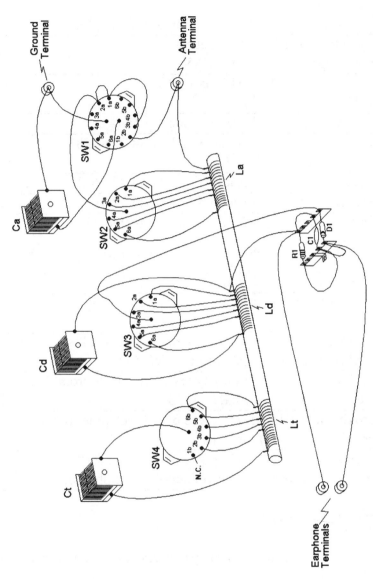

Notes:  Switches are viewed from the rear.
All four switches are the same type.
Half of the terminals on SW2, SW3, and SW4 were omitted for clarity.

Figure 4: Pictorial diagram of component connections

Table 1: Parts List

| # | Parts | Suggested Suppliers |
|---|-------|---------------------|
| 3 | 365 pF air dielectric variable capacitors | Xtal Set Society Part# 365 |
| 1 | Ferrite core, at least 5" x 11/32" dia | AES part# PC-72 |
| 1 | Crystal earphone | Xtal Set Society part# ear |
| 4 | 2 pole 6 position rotary switches | Radio Shack part# 275-1386 |
| 4 | Binding posts | Radio Shack part# 274-661 |
| 2 | Terminal strips | Radio Shack part# 274-688 |
| 1 | 1N34A germanium diode | Radio Shack part# 276-1123 |
| 1 | .001 μF capacitor | Radio Shack part# 272-126 |
| 1 | 10K resistor | Radio Shack part# 271-1126 |
| 1 | Spool of 30 gauge wire for coil | Radio Shack part# 278-502 |
| | Hook up wire for general connections | Radio Shack part#278-1216, 10ft. or AES part #S-W712 |
| 7 | Knobs for 1/4 inch diameter shafts | Many types are available from Radio Shack, AES. |
| 1 | Approximately 5 1/2" x 11" piece of 3/4 inch pine (or any other available wood) for base. | |
| 1 | Approximately 5 3/4" x 11" piece of masonite for front panel. A good source for this material is a clipboard. | |

## Miscellaneous Materials:

- Wood screws for mounting front panel and other components to chassis base.
- Small self-tapping screws for mounting variable capacitors to front panel.
- Silicone cement to mount coil to chassis base.
- Flat black spray paint and clear matte spray finish for front panel if desired.

# My Best Set Yet
by Carl Davis

I built my first xtal set when I was in the 7th grade. I made the galena xtal by setting it in lead. The coil of course was wound on the proverbial oatmeal carton and tapped. Only one station could be heard, but that was a great thrill. This was WDZ, then in Tuscola, IL. It featured what was then known as hillbilly music. Gene Autry's sidekick, Smiley Burnett, got his start there. A few kids said that they got Chicago, and building these sets was the current rage for a summer.

My next encounter was onboard various merchant ships in WWII. If I remember the circuit, they had a tapped coil to cover the lower BC band down to 200 Khz, for the marine band. The set had a catwhisker galena xtal on the front and also a variable capacitor. The ships were required to carry a crystal radio by law as a standby receiver. I could also get BC stations on it, so I listened to it quite a bit. The antenna on a typical ship was 200 feet long and 70-80 feet above salt water ground. The wire was braided copper, about ¼ inch in diameter, so you got good reception. Using the shipboard TRF regenerative receiver I could pull in WLW (800 Khz Cincinnati) from Rio de Janeiro, but only at a certain time just before dawn.

After many years, in about 1970, I again started experimenting. I built several sets using MRL (Modern Radio Laboratories) diagrams. They worked, but I did not get any dx with them. My main problems were limited antenna space; about 70 feet was the longest I could put up, and it was about 25 feet high. Also I had a KW BC station about 3 miles broadside to the antenna, so a grm coil was mandatory. These sets were various designs mainly consisting of a tapped solenoid type coil and various capacitors. Also, I used one with a basket weave coil but again with no great results.

Here is a description of my best set yet. Basically it consisted of 2 tuned, air-wound coils with variable coupling.

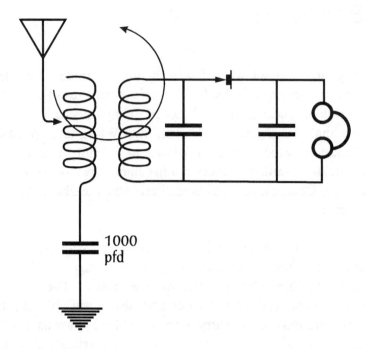

Figure 1: Schematic

## Construction

I made the air-wound coils as follows. A 1¼" diameter dowel was cut a few inches long, and then 9 holes were drilled in it at right angles to the surface, ¼" apart. In these holes I placed small dowel rods about 6" long, so that the coil form looked like a spoked wheel with no rim. The wire was #18 DCC which was woven around the spokes. I wound 50 turns on each coil. Then I glued these up with Hi Q coil cement. When the glue had set I removed the spokes and center piece and I had an air-wound coil.

The coil was fixed in place with a small piece of "plexiglas" glued between the windings. This was secured to the base, holding the coil in an upright position. The plexiglas is the type of plastic used in windows.
The other coil was movable, forwards and backwards. It had 2 small pieces of plexiglas (from storm windows) glued to it. This in turn

was attached to a ¼" dowel rod which slides in a tinkertoy piece (see Figure 3). This varied the coupling—I found that the optimum spacing was about ¼" to ½" between the coils.

Each coil was tuned by identical capacitors. These were taken from a surplus Air Force beacon receiver, the BC-453. The plates had an ellipsoid shape and the 3 sections were connected in parallel giving about 1000 pfd total. This enabled me to cover the whole BC band without a tapped coil. The antenna coil was in series with the capacitor and the detector in parallel. The dials were surplus from Fair Surplus, and had built-in reduction gear, although this isn't really needed.

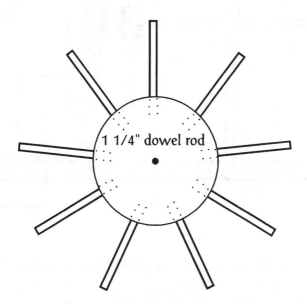

Figure 2: Coil form, 9 dowel rods, ¼" diameter, approximately 6" long

The rest of the circuit was conventional using a germanium diode and a grm coil. I put some plexiglas around the set to keep out the dust.

With this set the results were excellent for my location. I live about 120 miles out of Chicago. I can get 3 Chicago stations there any night; WGN, WBBM (the loudest), and WLS. Also WSM Nashville and WSB Atlanta are heard regularly. With good wintertime conditions, I have heard Toronto, Havana, Dallas, and a religious station near South America (Bon Aire). All this was with the same inadequate antenna. Hence my enthusiasm for this design.

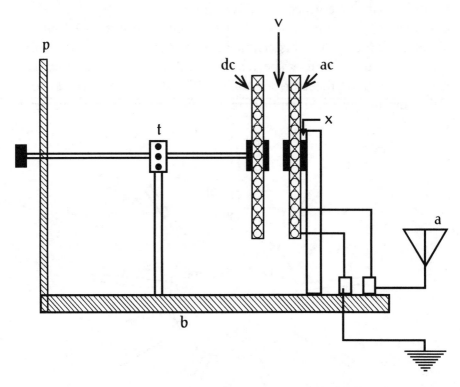

Figure 3: Pictorial diagram of adjustable coil coupling. *P*,panel; *t*, tinkertoy; *dc*, movable detector coil; *v*, variable spacing; *ac*, fixed antenna coil; *x*, plastic piece cemented to coil; *b*, base; *a*, antenna.

# Yesterday's Circuit Today's Parts
by William Simes

The set described here is based on one from Maurice J. Grainger's 1922 book, "Amateur Radio." It's a rather conventional circuit in that it rectifies the signal taken from an inductance which is adjusted to resonate with a capacitive antenna. The tuning coil is wound on a short length of PVC pipe with 22 AWG Beldsol magnet wire (Figure 1).

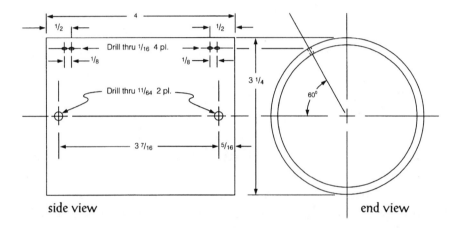

side view                                        end view

Figure 1: Coil form, 3 inch PVC (dimensions in inches)

Beldsol is a trade name for an enameled wire you can solder to without first removing the insulation. To wind the coil, first anchor the wire's starting end by lacing it snugly through the two small holes at one end of the coil form, then at each ten-turn interval twist a small loop in the wire to form a tap. Stagger these taps so they won't short together later when soldering connections to them. After making twelve taps at ten-turn intervals, make an additional twelve taps at one-turn intervals. Cut the winding wire a few inches beyond the final turn and thread it through the remaining small hole pair in the coil form to secure the winding. Pass the mounting bracket (Figure 2) through the coil. Fasten the coil form through the 2 larger holes in the form to the bracket with 6-32 machine screws.

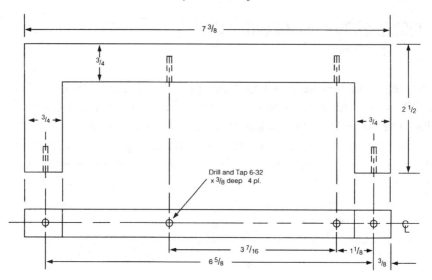

Figure 2: Coil mounting bracket, 1½ inch clear acrylic

The set shown in the Figure 3 schematic gives the operator a choice of detectors. 1) the use of 1N34A germanium diode wired inside phone plug, P1, which plugs into phone jack, J2 when the operator is in the no-nonsense-find-a-station-now mode, or, 2) the use of your favorite galena holder/cat whisker assembly for the operator who enjoys the nostalgia of searching for a hot spot of the xtal. The xtal detector assembly is not dimensioned in the sketches here. In laying out the panel of Figure 4, if you choose to use only the 1N34A detector, then P1, J2, and the holes for J2 and for the xtal assembly can be omitted. Keep your choice of options in mind when laying out the panel.

Once the panel is drilled, mount the components as indicated and complete the wiring. Notice that the stationary contacts of S3 simply parallel those of S2. As more of the coil is used by S2 for tuning, more taps become available to S3 for matching headphone impedance. The completed assembly is fastened with no. 6 wood screws in the enclosure shown in Figure 5. Once assembled, the box made of thick (¾ inch) material has the appearance of one made with thin (¼ inch) material.

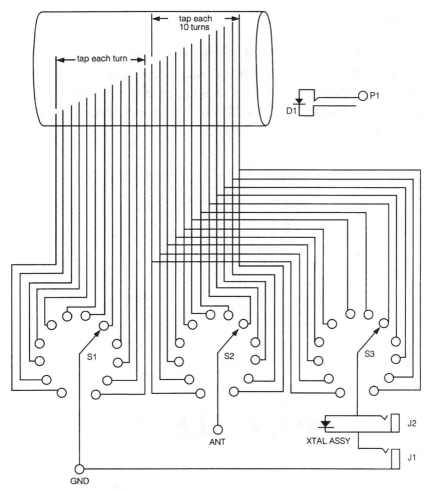

Figure 3: Schematic

Table 1: List of Materials

| S1, S2, S3 | rotary switches 1 pole 12 pos. | Electronic Supply CO |
|---|---|---|
| 3 ea | knobs, hexagonal 1 ¼" | Radio Shack 274-407 |
| D1 | 1N34A germanium diode | " "      276-1123 |
| P1 | phone plug ¼" | " "      274-1536 |
| J1, J2 | phone jack ¼" | " "      274-252 |
| 2 each | binding posts | " "      274-661 |
| 4 each | 6,32"x½" RH machine screws | |
| 4 each | #6x½"    RH wood screws | |

As required:

| | |
|---|---|
| 1/8 inch black acrylic | 1/2 inch clear acrylic |
| 3 inch PVC pipe | Wood glue Titebond II |
| Rosin-core solder | #20 AWG stranded hook-up wire |
| 3/4 inch clear pine | #24 AWG Beldsol solderable magnet |
| 1/8 inch masonite | wire |

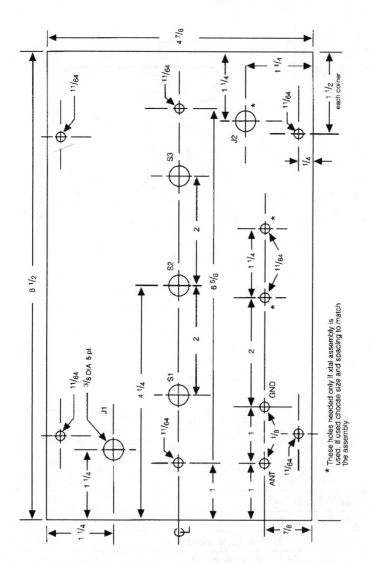

Figure 4: Panel (rear view), 1 1/8 inch black acrylic

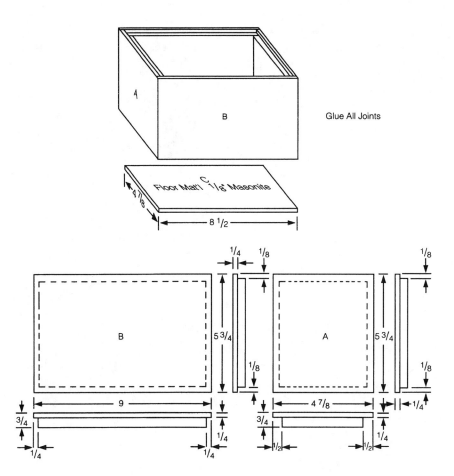

Figure 5: Enclosure

# A Magic Coil for Crystal Radios
by George Hails

This inexpensive, easy to build circuit will improve the reception of almost any crystal radio and can be used in many different ways. It is so easy to make and has so many uses you may want to make several at the same time. It can be used as a:

Wave Trap (Series, shunt or absorption)
Tuned Antenna Primary
Tuned Variable Antenna Coupler
Main Tuning Coil
Switched Series or Parallel Tuned Circuit
Design Aid

## Construction

The coil form is about 1" in diameter and 1 1/2" long. You can use a plastic pill container, cardboard tube, or cut sections from a plastic pipe. See Table 1 for the number of secondary turns (discussed below) for different size forms and wire sizes so you can choose coil-form dimensions to fit the material available.

Table 1: Number of secondary turns

| Diam. of Coil form | No. of turns | | | Length of form/inches | | |
|---|---|---|---|---|---|---|
| | 32 ga | 30 ga | 28 ga | 32 ga | 30 ga | 28 ga |
| 7/8" | 139 | 158 | 180 | 1 3/4 | 2 1/4 | 3 |
| 1" | 110 | 130 | 144 | 1 1/2 | 2 | 2 1/4 |
| 1 1/8" | 105 | 110 | 126 | 1 1/2 | 1 3/4 | 2 3/8 |

First drill, or punch, 4 tiny holes about 3/16" from each end of the coil form, as shown in Figure 1, to anchor the ends of both the primary and secondary windings. If the form is plastic you may be able to make the holes with a hot needle. To begin the primary winding, thread the end of the wire through the holes to anchor it before starting the winding. Leave about 8" of wire to make external connections.

Cut two pieces of tape and fold over the wire 1/4" sticking the remaining end to the form. Subsequent turns will further lock the tape and first turn in place, as shown in Figure 1. Wind all turns closely together.

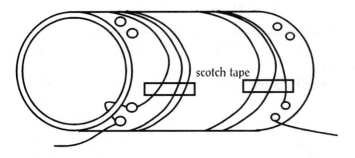

Figure 1: Coil form

Anchor the last turn similar to that of the first, leaving several inches at the free end for a connecting wire. You will have to loosen the last 2 or 3 turns of the winding to slip the tape underneath them, before final tightening and threading the wire through the holes. Cement the end turns with coil dope or other plastic cement.

Now, cut a strip of bond paper slightly wider than the length of the winding and wrap it around the coil, overlapping the ends about 3/8". Fasten these ends with Scotch tape or cement. This paper will protect the fine wire and provide a surface to wind the next winding which will be 15 to 25 turns of a heavier wire from 28 to 22 gauge.

Anchor this last (primary) winding in the remaining holes (as shown earlier in Figure 1) leaving enough wire on each end for external connections. This winding should be spread out evenly over the whole length of the coil.

The fine wire (secondary) coil should be tuned with a 350 to 450 picoFarad variable capacitor although good results can be had with many different variables. A tuning capacitor salvaged from an old radio would be excellent.

## Wavetrap

Many crystal radios have difficulty separating stations, but several circuit designs that sharpen the tuning also reduce the sound volume. By using this coil as a wave trap you can block out the unwanted station with little reduction in the desired signal. Wave traps can be connected in any of the ways shown in Figure 2, but Figure 2a is simple and works like magic! The small primary winding used here gives this coil its magic qualities. When connected in series with the

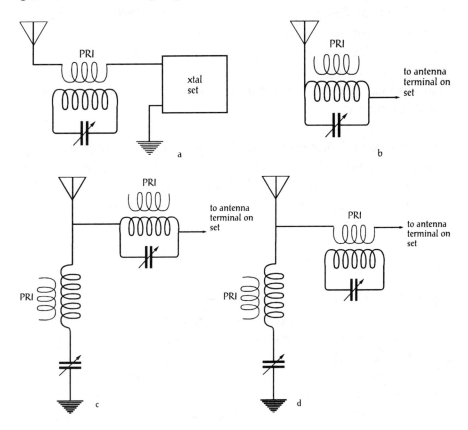

Figure 2: Wave trap schematics (PRI= primary winding)

antenna, as in Figure 2a, it acts like a transformer primary which will couple energy from the antenna into the tuned secondary winding only at the resonant frequency selected by the tuning capacitor. Energy will be absorbed principally at this frequency, so it will trap out an interfering station. A parallel resonant circuit has a very high resistance at its resonant frequency and, through transformer action, part of this resistance is inserted into the antenna winding, thus reducing the strength of the unwanted signal. This action is much more effective than the more commonly seen Figure 2b.

To operate a wave trap, first tune the crystal set to the interfering station, then tune the trap for minimum sound. While leaving the wave trap capacitor in its last position, tune the set for maximum sound from the desired station. You can then slightly vary the trap capacitor to further reduce the interference, but this is usually not necessary. The circuits of Figure 2c and 2d should kill the most powerful interfering signal but the magic of Figure 2a should suffice in most cases. The series resonant circuits act to short the interfering signals to ground.

Some of these circuits do not need the primary winding, but adding its few turns makes the coil more versatile. If you do not plan to use the primary in a particular application it can be left off. I usually make a half dozen of these coils at one time, including a couple without the primary.

## Acceptor Booster Circuit

Figure 3a shows a "booster", or acceptor, circuit—the series tuned circuit accepts the desired station while rejecting others. The parallel tuned circuit boosts the desired station while shunting all others to ground. Figure 3b will also boost a desired signal. Its primary or secondary can be connected to the antenna and ground terminals of the crystal set, although the primary connection usually works better. A small trimmer capacitor should be used when connecting to the secondary.

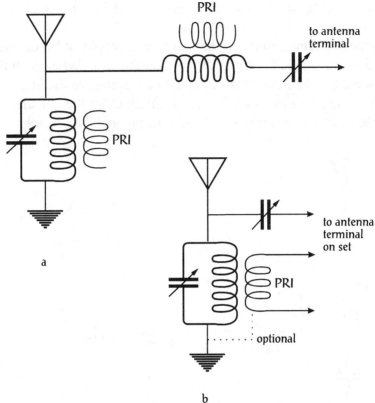

Figure 3: Booster circuit

## Tuned Antenna Primary

Many crystal radios do not have separate tuning for the antenna circuit, so they are missing a big improvement that can be made in selectivity and sensitivity. By connecting this magic coil with a variable capacitor as shown in Figure 4 you can add the tuned antenna circuit to many crystal radios.

This series resonant circuit greatly increases the antenna current at its resonant frequency (the desired station) making the received signal much louder and also reducing interference. The magic coil is so small it will usually slide inside the existing coil. If it will not, put it parallel and close the set's coil. In both positions it is best for the magic coil to be near the grounded end of the tuning coil.

The large resonant current in the magic coil couples a lot of energy through its magnetic field into the set's tuning coil. When both coils are resonant at the same frequency, both the current in the magic coil and the voltage in the set's coil are multiplied by their loaded "Q" factor to produce a sharply tuned and loud signal in the phones.

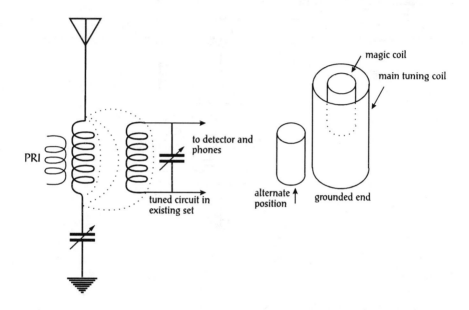

Figure 4:  Tuned antenna circuit

## Tuned Variable Antenna Coupler

By using the same circuit as in Figure 4, but varying the position of the magic coil, you can reduce the coupling to the set's coil and swap sensitivity for improved selectivity.  Since you have already increased sensitivity by tuning the antenna to resonance you can still have a strong signal. Just move the magic coil away from the coil in the set while tuned to a station suffering from interference, and the interfering station will diminish more than the desired station. If the magic coil is in the alternate position of Figure 4, then it can either be moved away from the other coil or tipped over to reduce the interference. When the two coils are at right angles to each other there will be minimum coupling and sharp selectivity. You will usually find some smaller angle desirable. Compare the "Wave Trap" circuits with this "Tuned Variable Antenna Coupler."

## Main Tuning Coil

The magic coil can be used as the main tuning coil of a compact crystal set radio. Although it is not the ideal main tuning coil it can be enhanced with some of the other circuits mentioned above, such as a wave trap, a tuned antenna primary, and a tuned antenna coupler. If you use the primary as an antenna coil and series tune it to the desired station as in Figure 5a it will give good reception. Depending on how short your antenna is, you may have to add a fixed capacitor in parallel with the variable antenna capacitor (Figure 5a). The circuit of 5b is quite selective, but the primary should have 30 or 40 turns.

## Switching From a Parallel to a Series Tuned Circuit

There are many cases where it would be convenient to be able to switch quickly from a parallel resonant to a series resonant circuit. Such an arrangement would be useful in some of the circuits described in this chapter. Figure 6 shows a double pole, double throw switch that will accomplish this switching. While Figure 6 shows a tuned circuit connected between an antenna and ground, the same two points could be connected to any external points. The above switching circuit was used in the earliest days of radio.

## Mounting and Housing the Magic Circuit

The magic coil can be permanently mounted in an existing, or planned, set or mounted in a small box as an auxiliary device. My wall-mounted antenna connection panel has two of these magic coil circuits connected to binding posts so I can insert them into any of my antenna leads while listening to or designing a new set.

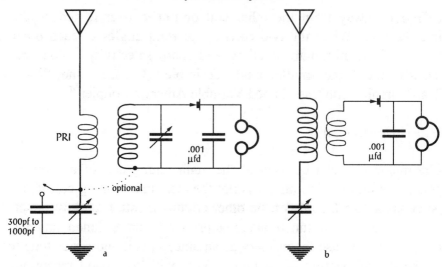

Figure 5: A fixed capacitor in parallel with the variable antenna capacitor

I have one mounted in a plastic refrigerator storage box with the variable capacitor bolted to the snap-on lid. The coil secondary is connected to the capacitor with 8 inch flexible leads and stored in the box. I just open the box to pull the coil out to connect to an existing set in any of the ways described. Clip leads are used to connect the primary and a double pole double throw switch mounted on the lid. This provides the series or parallel connection mentioned above for the secondary.

These coils should be at least 1 inch away from metal such as a variable capacitor or a metal shield panel. If one has unwanted coupling to another

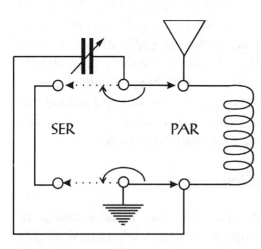

Figure 6: Switching between parallel resonant and series resonant circuit

coil, turn the coils at right angles to one another. Since the coil is always used with a variable capacitor, it can be mounted on the capacitor if stiff connecting wire is crimped on the coil form and soldered on both ends. Solid #22 to #18 wire will hold the coil 1 to 3 inches away from the capacitor with little movement.

The many uses of the magic coil make it well worth the little effort to build it. Try it and you will understand why it was named MAGIC!

## About the Author

George Hails started building crystal radios before the germanium diode was invented. The total is now well over 100 sets. Retired from a career in the long distance communication industry he now collects ancient test equipment and old books and magazines covering the development of radio and electronics. His grandkids also build xtal sets!

# Antenna-Ground System
by Mark Zechar

The performance of crystal radio receivers is highly dependent upon the incoming signal applied to them. This is because they have no amplification capabilities. Any factor which diminishes the incoming signal reduces the effectiveness of the receiver.

The antenna is the mechanism which intercepts the radio signal from the atmosphere and applies it to the crystal radio receiver. For a specific incoming signal strength at the receiving site and for a given antenna design and installation, there is a maximum signal interception capability. For crystal radio receivers, it is mandatory that we do everything possible to maximize the antenna signal interception capability.

There are several factors which affect the signal strength at the receiving antenna site. These are usually outside the realm of control of the antenna designer/installer. They include time of day, time of the year, amount of sunshine, distance from the transmitting station, and obstructions between the receiving and transmitting antennas. Then there are several factors which affect the antenna effectiveness itself. The antenna designer/installer may have some degree of control over these factors, but there may also be physical constraints to which the antenna must conform. This second set of factors includes height of the antenna above ground, length of the antenna, isolation from other entities which also act as antennas, placement of the antenna inside or outside a structure, and grounding of the crystal radio receiver.

One thing we can do to insure the maximum effectiveness of the antenna/radio receiver system is to connect the receiver to earth ground. The earth ground is the reference for all radio systems.

Consider the situation when the receiver is not tied electrically to earth ground. Figure 1 illustrates a simple crystal receiver which is

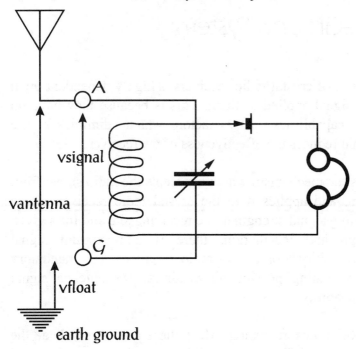

where:  vantenna is the voltage of the radio signal intercepted by the antenna.

     vsignal is the voltage of the radio signal applied to the receiver.

     vfloat is the voltage on the non-antenna node (node G) of the radio receiver.

Figure 1: "Floating" crystal receiver

"floating" with respect to earth ground. The voltage the receiver responds to is vsignal, the voltage impressed across the tuned circuit (the parallel combination of the coil and the variable capacitor). Vsignal is the difference between vantenna and vfloat.

   vantenna = vsignal + vfloat  (from Figure 1).

Applying some algebraic manipulation,

vsignal = vantenna - vfloat.

This example illustrates an important concept; the signal being applied to a "floating" crystal receiver is less than the signal intercepted by the antenna. This condition reduces the effectiveness of the radio receiver.

The actual value of vfloat is not known. In some instances it may possible that it is very close to zero volts. But we do not know in all situations what it is and therefore can not guarantee anything about it.

Conversely, in Figure 2, when the non-antenna node of the receiver is tied electrically to earth ground, the received signal voltage (vantenna) is the same as vsignal, the signal applied to the crystal receiver. This is because vfloat is at the same potential as earth ground and is zero volts. The maximum signal possible from the antenna is applied to the receiver.

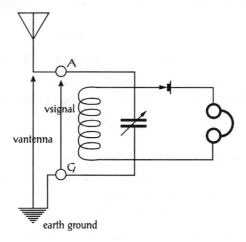

Figure 2: Crystal receiver, non-antenna node of receiver with path to ground

There are several possibilities for establishing an earth ground. Basically, this involves burying good electrical conductors in the ground and insuring that as much surface area of the conductors as possible is in contact with the earth. Usually the conductor of choice is copper—it is readily available, and it is one of the better electrical conductors.

One of the possible ground implementations involves driving a series of ground rods into the ground (spaced about one to two feet apart) and tying them together electrically with wire or braid. (Use stranded wire and sweat solder to the ground rods). Connect this ground system to the receiver with either braid, ground strap or stranded wire. Keep this distance as short as practical. This will normally necessitate routing the conductor from the receiver to the ground system through a wall or a window.

A second possible implementation (Figure 3) would be to bury 3/4 inch copper water pipes (Type M) in a radial pattern (maybe two to sixteen pipes). As above, tie the exposed pipe ends together and connect to the receiver with either braid, ground strap, or stranded wire. Again the conductor routing will probably be through a wall or a window.

A third possible implementation is a radial pattern of heavy copper wire either buried or laid on top of the ground with a ground rod in the center of the pattern. Again, tie the center ends together and to the ground rod before routing to the receiver.

A technique to improve conductivity in the earth (once the ground system is buried) is to introduce water and/or minerals into the ground in the vicinity of the buried conductors. The minerals become dissolved in the ground water/moisture and enhance the soil conductivity (or lowers the resistance between the buried conductors and the earth).

For more information about these ground systems, the *Practical Antenna Handbook* by Joseph J. Carr is recommended.

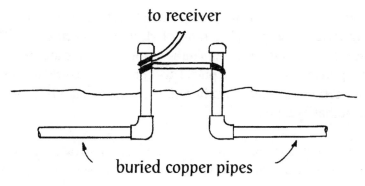

to receiver

buried copper pipes

Figure 3: Earth ground

All of the above assumes that you have the property and the inclination to implement one of the proposed techniques. Often times this is not the case. There are alternatives. These alternatives may not yield the equivalent performance, but they are simpler to implement.

One effective matrix of copper is the cold water supply distribution system of a city water works. Conductivity is enhanced by virtue of water inside the pipes. Also, substantial surface area is in contact with the earth. An effective tie-in to this ground system is to wrap bare wire around a cold water pipe (clean the copper first) and tie the other end of the wire to the crystal receiver. However, this may not be convenient because access to a cold water pipe would normally be in the kitchen or bathroom. (A note about cold water pipes: if you have galvanized pipes instead of copper, by all means use them. Plastic pipe, of course, is not suitable as a ground system).

Hot water pipes should not be used because they do not tie directly to the water distribution system. They terminate into a hot water heater. Natural gas pipes should not be used as they are a safety concern as well as being interrupted by a meter before they tie into the underground distribution system.

Another possibility is to tie into the "equipment" ground of the house wiring system. The "equipment" ground is a system of wires which accomplish an electrical connection between earth ground and the third terminal (inverted half-moon) of all duplex receptacles. It's purpose is to provide the capability for any apparatus (or equipment) plugged into a receptacle to connect to earth ground. This facility serves to protect against shock hazards should a piece of equipment malfunction.

The requirement is that any apparatus, plugged into a receptacle, whose case can conduct electricity, must have that case connected to earth ground. An example would be a microwave oven or refrigerator. (These cases are metal). Most apparatus/appliances are enclosed in non-conductive (plastic) cases and thus do not employ the third duplex terminal. An example would be a hand-held hairdryer.

As a side-note, if the boxes in the wall which contain the duplex receptacles are metal, these boxes are also connected to earth ground through the "equipment ground" system.

Depending upon your locale and electrical code requirements, the "equipment" ground is connected to a ground rod and/or a cold water pipe (Figure 4). A ground rod is a copper-clad steel rod 5/8 to 3/4 inch in diameter, 8 feet long. It is driven into the ground, and a copper wire is attached to the exposed rod above ground.

There are several ways to tie into this system. One is to loop bare wire under the screwhead of either a duplex or "on-off" switch coverplate (either scraping the paint on the screw away or substituting an unpainted screw). Be careful not to crack plastic cover plates by tightening down the screw too much.

A second technique is to construct a plug with a wire or braid attached only to the ground prong. (Take extreme precautions to insure the wire does not touch the other attachments to the blades within the plug housing). Optionally, solder an alligator clip to the other end to connect to the crystal receiver (Figure 5).

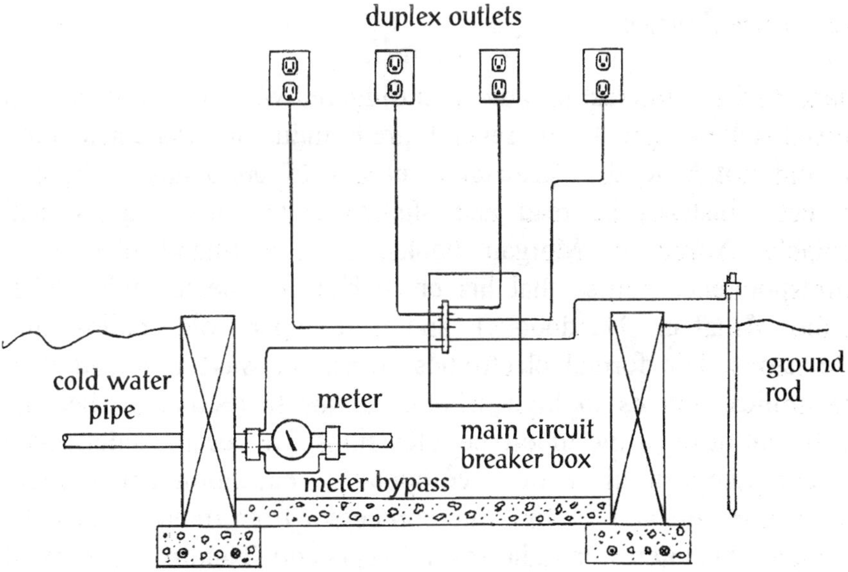

duplex outlets

cold water pipe

meter

meter bypass

main circuit breaker box

ground rod

Figure 4: Typical residential equipment grounding scheme

Any connection to earth ground via a cold water pipe or the electrical "equipment" ground system will more than likely be a physically longer run to reach earth than the "home-made" copper burial ground systems. This will degrade performance to some extent.

Finally, a rule to remember for receiver-only ground systems is that something, even if not optimum, is better than nothing.

No connections to these terminals

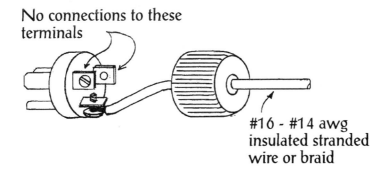

#16 - #14 awg insulated stranded wire or braid

Figure 5: Construction of a ground "plug"

## About the Author

Mark Zechar's interest in radio was triggered when he constructed a crystal radio as part of his seventh grade industrial arts curriculum. He did not have the financial resources to build any additional projects. Instead, he read and studied electronics a great deal (notably Alfred P. Morgan books, a second-hand electronics correspondence course that his uncle had completed, and ARRL Radio Amateur Handbooks) and tore apart old radios and televisions. His formal electronics education was continued with electronics courses in high school. It was there that he became proficient at repairing tube-type televisions. He became sidetracked on computers at his college co-operative education employment (minicomputers and the first microprocessor from Intel). Finally, he rekindled his interest in radio several years ago. To him, the irony of the situation is that he now has the financial resources and the desire—plus the electronics education to design and construct radio receivers—but is short of time to do so!

Mark was born in 1951, in Dayton, Ohio. He graduated from the University of Cincinnati with a B.S.E.E. in 1974, and has been employed as an electrical engineer ever since. He lives in the Cincinnati area.

# The Design and Construction of a Ferrite Loopstick Inductor for an AM Broadcast Receiver
by Ross Wollrab

Trying many different kinds of coils is a favorite pastime of crystal set enthusiasts. Although a coil can be wound on any form, from an old oatbox to a PVC pipe to ferrite, a hard non-conductive substance is a choice many experimenters have tried. Although it is possible to buy ferrite loopstick inductors, it is also possible to design and build your own. Some AM broadcast receivers employ a parallel inductor-capacitor (LC) tank circuit to tune the receiver as depicted in Figure 1.

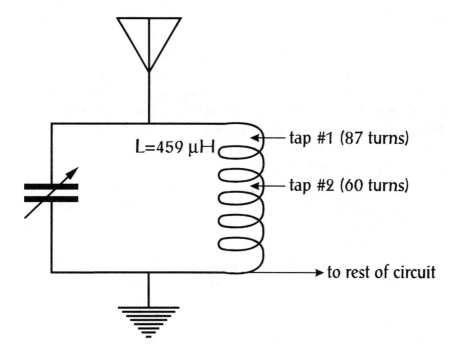

L=459 μH

tap #1 (87 turns)

tap #2 (60 turns)

to rest of circuit

Figure 1: Parallel inductor-capacitor (LC) tank circuit

Referring to Figure 1, when the upper lead of the circuit is tapped at tap #1 (87 turns from the bottom of the coil), the ferrite loopstick inductor receives the maximum incoming signal strength but is lower in tuning selectivity. Moving the upper lead to tap #2 (60 turns, approximately 2/3 the total number of turns) reduces the incoming signal strength since the number of inductance coils is reduced, but improves the selectivity of tuning.

For our ferrite loopstick design I used one cylindrical ferrite rod that had a 1/2 inch outside diameter and had a 4 inch length. I obtained the rod from Amidon Associates (AA) which is listed in the vendor section at the end e (AA part number R61-050-400). The advantage of making your own loopstick inductor is that you can include taps to improve the inductor's selectivity.

I tightly wrapped 102 turns of number 22 AWG enamel wire on the ferrite rod creating a tap (loop) at 60 turns and a second tap at 87 turns. Count your turns carefully. I started the windings at about 1/2 inch from one end. I also left about 6 inches of wire protruding from each end of the coil to use for eventual hookup wires in the circuit. After the first 25 to 30 turns you can wrap one end with a piece of electrical tape to hold the windings in place. After finishing the winding, I took a piece of sandpaper and sanded the enamel off the tap and off each end of the hookup wires of the coil so I would have good electrical connections. Next I measured the inductance of the ferrite loopstick with a digital LRC meter. It turned out that 102 turns were too many, with a measured inductance of over 500 $\mu$H. There are several factors that affect the inductance mentioned in the AA catalog. One factor is the spacing between adjacent turns on the rod. Make sure you wind your coils tightly. The calculated number of turns only gives an estimate of what is actually needed. To lower the inductance I took off several turns until I had a measured inductance of 459 $\mu$H. Finally, I clipped off the excess wire, sanded the enamel off the tip of the hookup lead, and wrapped the other finished end with a piece of electrical tape to hold the windings in place.

The following table lists the final number of turns needed, along with the measured values of inductance, for the ferrite loopstick inductor that I designed and built. These values will give you a good ferrite loopstick inductor for use in an AM broadcast receiver. Keep in mind that this is only for the specific ferrite rod whose part number was mentioned earlier.

Table 1:  Ferrite Loopstick Inductance

| Tap | Turns | L measured* (microhenries) |
|-----|-------|---------------------------|
| Tap#1 | 87 turns | 459 |
| Tap#2 | 60 turns | 245 |

*Measured with a Scope Model 680 LRC Meter

If you obtain a ferrite rod of a different size, you can still determine how many turns you need with some experimenting, and if you are up to it, a few formulas.

With the effective $A_L$ of the rod we can determine the approximate number of turns needed for our ferrite loopstick from the following formula (which comes from the AA catalog):

$$N = 1000\left[\frac{desired\ L(mh)}{A_L\left(mH/1000t\right)}\right]^{1/2} \quad \text{(Formula 1)}$$

Where,

N=The number of turns needed for the loopstick

L=The maximum loopstick inductance desired in millihenries
=0.450 mH

$A_L$=The ferrite rod design value=43 mH/1000turns (from AA catalog)

We can now calculate the approximate number of turns needed for our loopstick:

$$N = 1000\left(\frac{0.450}{43}\right)^{1/2}$$

N = 102 turns

Next we can use Table 2 to determine the length of coil windings. This table also comes from the AA catalog.

Table 2: Copper Wire Table

| Wire Size AWG | Wire Diameter inches (enamel) | Circular mil area | Turns per linear inch | Turns per square cm |
|---|---|---|---|---|
| 8 | .1285 | 16510 | 7.6 | |
| 10 | .1019 | 10380 | 10.7 | 13.8 |
| 12 | .0808 | 6530 | 12 | 21.7 |
| 14 | .064 | 4107 | 15 | 34.1 |
| 16 | .0508 | 2583 | 18.9 | 61.2 |
| 18 | .0403 | 1624 | 23.6 | 79.1 |
| 20 | .0319 | 1022 | 29.4 | 124 |
| 22 | .0253 | 642 | 37 | 186 |
| 24 | .0201 | 404 | 46.3 | 294 |
| 26 | .0159 | 254 | 58 | 465 |
| 28 | .0126 | 160 | 72.7 | 728 |
| 30 | .01 | 101 | 90.5 | 1085 |
| 32 | .0079 | 63 | 113 | 1628 |
| 34 | .0063 | 40 | 141 | 2480 |
| 36 | .005 | 25 | 175 | 3876 |
| 38 | .0039 | 16 | 224 | 5736 |
| 40 | .0031 | 10 | 382 | 10077 |

From Table 2 and the turns per linear inch value we can determine the approximate number of inches of wire we need to wind on the loopstick. I used 22 AWG wire for the coil I designed and built:

102 turns * (1 inch/37.0 turns) = 2.76 inches

This gives us an estimate of how wide the coil will be and the length of ferrite rod needed. I obtained my enamel covered 22 AWG magnet wire from Radio Shack (RS). The part number is #278-1345.

With the parts previously listed, the previous instructions, and Tables 1 and 2 you should now be able to build a ferrite loopstick inductor for the AM broadcast band. Alternatively, with formula 3 you can approximate the number of turns needed for any inductance under 450 µH by substituting the desired inductance for LMAX. You can then use an LRC meter or bridge to determine the exact number of turns needed.

In most AM broadcast receivers it is typical to use a 365 pF (365 x $10^{-12}$ F) variable capacitor to tune the circuit to its resonant frequency. As an example, I measured the capacitance of a variable capacitor I salvaged from an old Philco radio. I got the following results:

The resonant frequency of tuning for the parallel LC circuit depicted in Figure 1 is given by,

$$f_o = \frac{1}{2\pi\sqrt{LC}} \quad (\text{Formula 2})$$

Where 
$f_O$ = The resonant frequency of tuning
$L$ = The inductance of the ferrite loopstick.
$C$ = The capacitance of the variable capacitor.
*Measured with a Scope Model 680 LRC Meter

From Formula 2 we can solve for the inductance of the ferrite loopstick.

$$L = \frac{1}{C}\left[\frac{1}{2\pi f_o}\right]^2 \quad (\text{Formula 3})$$

The frequency range over which the AM broadcast band covers is from 535 kHz (535 x $10^3$ Hz) to 1605 kHz (1605 x $10^3$ Hz). From Formula 3, the minimum and maximum values of the variable capacitor's capacitance ($C_{MIN}$ and $C_{MAX}$), and the lower frequency ($f_{oMIN}$) and upper frequency ($f_{oMAX}$) of the broadcast band, we can now calculate the approximate minimum inductance ($L_{MAX}$) and maximum inductance needed for our ferrite loopstick to tune over the AM broadcast band.

$$L_{MIN} = \frac{1}{C_{MAX}}\left[\frac{1}{2\pi f_{oMAX}}\right]^2$$

$$L_{MIN} = \frac{1}{368 \cdot 10^{-12}\,F}\left[\frac{1}{2\pi\left(1605 \cdot 10^3\,hz\right)}\right]^2$$

$$L_{MIN} = 26.7 \cdot 10^{-6}\,H = 26.7\,\mu H$$

$$L_{MAX} = \frac{1}{C_{MIN}}\left[\frac{1}{2\pi f_{oMIN}}\right]^2$$

$$L_{MAX} = \frac{1}{21 \cdot 10^{-12}\,F}\left[\frac{1}{2\pi\left(535 \cdot 10^3\,hz\right)}\right]^2$$

$$L_{MAX} = 421 \cdot 10^{-6}\,H = 421\,\mu H$$

Theoretically, we would want a ferrite loopstick inductor whose inductance varies from 26.7 µH to 421 µH to approximately cover the AM broadcast band. However, we need to allow for some overlap for the ferrite loopstick inductor by making it vary from 0-450 µH to cover the entire AM broadcast band. Ferrite loopstick inductors for the AM broadcast band usually have a maximum inductance of 450 µH.

❖

# Vendor List

Xtal Set Society
www.midnightscience.com
1-800-927-1771

365pf variable capacitors
Crystal earplugs, 2000 ohm
headsets, galena
crystals, catswhiskers

Amidon Associates
PO Box 25867
Santa Ana, CA 92799
(714) 850-4660
call or write for catalog

ferrite rods

Antique Electronic Supply
6221 S. Maple Ave.
Tempe, AZ 85283
fax (800) 706-6789
phone (602) 820-5411
call or write for free catalog

coils, trimmer capacitors,
germanium diodes,
crystal earphone, knobs,
fahnesstock clips, antenna kits

Antique Radio Classified
P.O. Box 2
Carlisle, MA 01741
(508) 371-0512
call or write for free copy

monthly magazine for antique
radio collectors

Circuit Specialists, Inc.
P.O. Box 3047
Scottsdale, AZ 85271
(800) 528-1417

trimmer capacitors, tuning
capacitors, diodes

Lindsay Publications
P.O. Box 538
Bradley, IL 60915-0538
(815) 935-5353

catalog of reprints and unusual
technical books

Midco                          variety of crystal set parts
Dr. B.A. Turke
P.O. Box 2288
Hollywood, FL 33022
(954) 925-3670
send $2 for catalog

Monitoring Times               magazine for shortwave radio
Grove Enterprises              and scanning enthusiasts
P.O. Box 98
Brasstown, NC 28902
(800) 438-8155

Mouser Electronics             crystal earphones, diodes
1-800-346-6873

Radio Shack                    1N34 germanium diode,
                               terminal strips, capacitors,
                               switches, wire

Rainy Day Books                old reprints and hard to find
P.O. Box 775                   books
Fitzwilliam, NH 03447-0775
(603)-585-3448

# THE XTAL SET SOCIETY

The Xtal Set Society *Newsletter*, bi-monthly, one year
subscription. Postage is included.

$ 12.95

International subscriptions please remit US$19.00,
Canadians please remit US$14.00.

*Volume I & II* of the Society Newsletter, 12 issues,
ending May, 1993.                                         $ 19.95

*The Crystal Set Handbook* and Volume III of the
Society Newsletter, three issues, ending Nov. 1993.       $ 11.95

*Volume IV* of the Society Newsletter, six issues,
ending November 1994.                                     $ 10.95

*Crystal Sets: Volume V* of the Society Newsletter,
six issues, ending November 1995.                         $ 10.95

*Crystal Radio: History, Fundamentals, and Design*       $ 11.95

*Crystal Set Building & More: Volume 6 & 7*               $ 15.95

*Crystal Set Loopers a 3 Tuber & More: Volume 8*         $ 15.95

*Crystal Set Projects: 15 Radio Projects You Can Build*  $ 14.95

Shipping and handling                                     $ 3.50
International orders e-mail or write for shipping.

**The Xtal Set Society**
VISA/MC accepted  e-mail: xtalset@midnightscience.com
**www.midnightscience.com**
**1-800-927-1771**

## THE CRYSTAL SET HANDBOOK

There is nothing else like this handbook. It takes the reader beyond the basics and discusses the math and mechanisms behind the mystery of the crystal set. "This book is written for crystal set enthusiasts, radio amateurs, first-time radio experimenters, and electronics students. I wrote it to encourage design, building, and experimentation" —Phil Anderson. Contents of the book include an introduction to the crystal set with a simple oat box project, formulas for coil inductance and coil Q, a procedure for measuring coil capacitance, introductory and advanced chapters on L-C circuit matching, and Volume III of the Xtal Set Society Newsletter (issues 13-15). 8 x 5½ paperback, 133 pages, $11.95.

## CRYSTAL SETS:VOLUME V

Volume V of the Society newsletter includes six issues ending November 1995. Great for new members to get current, those wanting a bound copy for their reference bookshelf, or as a gift to get a friend started. Contents include: The Design of Unpowered AM Receivers, Radio Outfit in a Headset, A Crystal Set Revisited-Reconstructed, Grounded Loopstick Tuner, The Matching Secret, and lots of membership correspondence. 8½ x 5½ paperback, $10.95.

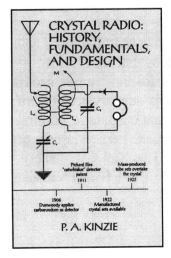

# CRYSTAL RADIO: HISTORY, FUNDAMENTALS, & DESIGN

Written by a long-time member of the Xtal Set Society, Mr. Phil Kinzie, this book chronicles the fascinating history and development of the crystal detector, including the reasons for its brief dominance of the radio market after the turn of the century. Starting with the discovery of solid-state rectification and then through the development of the crystal detector, the reader learns about great inventors such as Pickard, Braun, Dunwoody, and others. Radio fundamentals such as antennas, ground, lightning protection, tuned circuits, and detection are covered for the beginner. The unending compromise between selectivity and sensitivity is discussed for the crystal set designer. Advanced topics such as the use of multi-tuned circuits and wave traps follow for the serious experimenter. 8½ x 5½ paperback, 124 pages, $11.95.

**VOLUME I & II** Don't miss out on these great Originals! Now in our seventh year, the original 6 issues still hold their own. Included in Volume One, a complete set of plans for a "Modern Day Crystal Set," including pc layout and audio amplification. Why did the sets of the 1920's work anyway? Crystal sets and wireless, 1905-1928. A barebones crystal set, compact! Matching your antenna and set for maximum signal reception. The second volume includes: The Lead Pencil Detector! What's the minimum detectable signal? Detector Biasing for improved sensitivity. Double-tuned circuit crystal sets. The Universal Crystal Set. FM crystal sets? The electrolytic detector. The coherer revisited. The Miller '595' Tuner revisited. A galena detector from Italy. 8½ x 11, spiral binding, 70 pages, $19.95.

The Xtal Set Society is dedicated to once again building and experimenting with radio electronics, often—but not always—through the use of the crystal set, the basis for most modern day radio apparatus. The Society newsletter helps support our goal of producing excellent quality technical books that encourage learning and building. To join the society and receive one year (6 issues) of the bi-monthly newsletter, remit $12.95 to The Xtal Set Society. Canadians, please remit US $14.00. Outside the US and Canada please remit US $19.00. Thank You!

## The Xtal Set Society
VISA/MC accepted  e-mail: xtalset@midnightscience.com
### www.midnightscience.com
### 1-800-927-1771

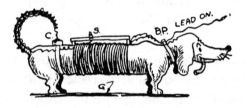